D0674149

DESIGN AND FUNCTION
AT THE THRESHOLD
OF LIFE: The Viruses

ACADEMIC PAPERBACKS*

BIOLOGY

Edited by ALVIN NASON

Design and Function at the Threshold of Life: The Viruses
   HEINZ FRAENKEL-CONRAT
Time, Cells, and Aging   BERNARD L. STREHLER
Isotopes in Biology   GEORGE WOLF
Life: Its Nature, Origin, and Development   A. I. OPARIN

MATHEMATICS

Edited by W. MAGNUS and A. SHENITZER

Finite Permutation Groups   HELMUT WIELANDT
Introduction to *p*-Adic Numbers and Valuation Theory
   GEORGE BACHMAN
Quadratic Forms and Matrices   N. V. YEFIMOV
Elements of Abstract Harmonic Analysis
   GEORGE BACHMAN
Noneuclidean Geometry   HERBERT MESCHKOWSKI

PHYSICS

Edited by D. ALLAN BROMLEY

Elementary Dynamics of Particles   H. W. HARKNESS
Elementary Plane Rigid Dynamics   H. W. HARKNESS
Crystals: Their Role in Nature and in Science   CHARLES BUNN
Potential Barriers in Semiconductors   B. R. GOSSICK
Mössbauer Effect: Principles and Applications
   GUNTHER K. WERTHEIM

* Most of these volumes are also available in a cloth bound
edition.

DESIGN AND FUNCTION AT THE THRESHOLD OF LIFE: The Viruses

HEINZ FRAENKEL-CONRAT

VIRUS LABORATORY, UNIVERSITY OF CALIFORNIA, BERKELEY, CALIFORNIA

ACADEMIC PRESS · NEW YORK AND LONDON

DRAKE MEMORIAL LIBRARY
STATE UNIVERSITY COLLEGE
BROCKPORT. NEW YORK

100798
C.1

COPYRIGHT © 1962, BY ACADEMIC PRESS INC.

ALL RIGHTS RESERVED

First Printing, 1962
Second Printing, 1963
Third Corrected Printing, 1964

NO PART OF THIS BOOK MAY BE REPRODUCED IN ANY FORM
BY PHOTOSTAT, MICROFILM, OR ANY OTHER MEANS,
WITHOUT WRITTEN PERMISSION FROM THE PUBLISHERS.

ACADEMIC PRESS INC.
111 FIFTH AVENUE, NEW YORK 3, NEW YORK

United Kingdom Edition published by
ACADEMIC PRESS INC. (LONDON) LTD.
BERKELEY SQUARE HOUSE, LONDON W.1

Library of Congress Catalog Card Number 62–13110

PRINTED IN THE UNITED STATES OF AMERICA

Preface

IN THE COURSE OF THE LAST twenty-five years the physical and biological sciences have undergone a dramatic change. From a hobby or spare time activity of a few enthusiasts these sciences have proceeded, for better or for worse, to represent the daily concern and livelihood of many thousands of men and women all over the world. Governments support these activities with billions of dollars. These facts induce feelings of pride and joy in the heart of the active scientist, although an occasional sensation of awe, or even fear, may justly disturb him. This concern may be lessened, however, when he considers that probably at least 90% of the current investment of time and money is not directed toward scientific research, but rather toward the practical development of scientific discoveries. The line between this and pure technology is hard to draw. Science reporters find it easier to discuss the finished product than the fundamental principles. The result of this is a grossly distorted picture of the world of science. Rarely does the layman get a true presentation of the purposes and processes of fundamental research, or see how new discoveries may originate from unexpected observations and erroneous theories.

This little book, written at spare moments during an active research period, tries to rectify this false impression. My research interests at this time happen to closely approach one of the main streams (to avoid the term "band wagon") of progress in a field in which our knowledge is growing at

v

100798

an unprecedented rate. When I decided to do some general writing on this subject three possible paths seemed open. I could produce either a scholarly treatise addressed to my fellow scientists; or a breathless account of the latest developments for whoever could follow; or finally, I could attempt to describe the developments in a relaxed and leisurely manner, explaining all technical terms so that the educated layman might understand what I was talking about. This latter course was chosen. However, my preoccupation with other activities has led to a very abbreviated account, and for this I must apologize. Much interesting or important material has fallen by the wayside. On the other hand, some very new material that has not yet been digested by the scientific world has been included.

This little book is not intended to satisfy anybody. It is hoped that it may whet the appetite of the reader, so he will want to delve into some of the more scientific literature listed at the end of the book. It is also hoped that it will give him a more realistic concept of the path of a rapidly advancing science, benefiting from trial and error, discovery and correction, and disregarding frontiers and curtains. If this effort leads one bright young man or woman to consider a scientific career, then it was worthwhile. For we need such young people who like to think and play to further the advance of science, and thereby justify the great expenditure of public funds.

I would like to express my indebtedness to R. C. Williams and J. Toby for supplying Figs. 1 and 3A-D, to H. L. Nixon for Fig. 3E, to R. Hart for Fig. 19. Most of the drawings were made by B. Bratton. Figures 15, 18, and 20 were kindly supplied by R. Valens.

H. Fraenkel-Conrat

Berkeley, April, 1962

Contents

Introduction

THIS LITTLE BOOK DEALS
with the chemistry of viruses. Viruses come in many sizes,
differing almost as widely as all the elements from hydrogen
to uranium in regard to weight and complexity. At present
we know a fair amount about the simpler viruses which
account for many diseases of plants, and some of animals
and man, including poliomyelitis. These simpler viruses
will therefore represent our primary topic with frequent
and particular reference to tobacco mosaic virus, the best
known of the lot. Now some might ask: Who cares about
a virus that afflicts tobacco plants, and for what reason?
One answer which such a questioner would readily accept
would be: The tobacco grower cares, and for monetary
reasons. However, speaking for many research men all over
the world who work with this virus without getting or
wishing support from the Tobacco Growers Association, I
would like to give two better, though quite different, an-
swers to that question.

One frequently employed line of defense goes about as
follows: all viruses obey similar principles. Thus, everything we learn about one particular virus, even though it
afflicts tobacco plants, will also teach us something about
the viruses that our physician blames for our aches and
pains. You can never tell what unexpected practical use or
cure may come from the research of one of these ivory tower
scientists. Some practically-minded people had better look

1

and listen to what is going on in pure science, so it won't all go to waste.

While there is some validity to the first part of this argument, I would like to present quite another purpose for the study of, as well as for the reading about, tobacco mosaic virus. Certain instincts, such as that of procreation, are shared by man and all animals; certain others, such as curiosity, man shares with but a few of the better kind of animals; finally, of the power of reasoning, man may well be the sole possessor. Research relies on a combination of these latter two attributes and is the domain only of *Homo sapiens*. He wonders what will be around the corner, and when he finds out, he tries to explain how it got there and what it represents. Obviously, man reading accounts of man's doings will be very much more interested in his searching into and his mental groping with the unknown than in his lower instincts, such as his procreational activity. (Clearly, therefore, the composition of most best seller lists must be quite erroneous.)

Yes, I would like to defend research for its own sake, this fascinating interplay of intuition, reasoning, and experimentation. I don't think scientists ought to be ashamed to confess that they enjoy their work. More often than not they call it play and use the same terms as the gambler or the sportsman. As these, they also enjoy sharing their experiences with others. Finally, they enjoy hearing of the triumphs and downfalls of their colleagues and competitors. These latter aspects of the scientific sport usually proceed according to the impersonal and humorless rules concerned with publication in the technical journals. However, the writing of supposedly readable accounts may be regarded as part of the game and, to be enjoyable, it must be personal and not entirely free of prejudice and temperament. The main purpose of such an account is the hope that it may contribute to the vicarious satisfaction of the curiosity of those unfortunate people who were prevented by circumstances from becoming research scientists and instead turned into bank presidents, dentists, milkmen, research administrators, politicians, or small-time thieves. Particularly, however, one must hope to kindle the spark of curiosity in young men and women who have not yet selected a profession in the hope that this might lead them to consider a scientific career. For here work is play, and nevertheless the pay checks come regularly.

The brief history
of virology,
briefly surveyed

THE WORD VIRUS WAS USED from ancient times until about 100 years ago to denote all sorts of noxious or poisonous agents. About the middle of the last century, serious attempts had gotten under way to investigate the causes and effects of biological phenomena, and it then became evident that there existed several quite different classes of harmful agents. One class of substances presented no conceptional problem—the typical poisons or toxins, varying from those simple in chemical composition, such as carbon monoxide and potassium cyanide, to chemically complex organic molecules, including proteins. Another class, the discovery of which had an enormous impact on the development of the biological sciences, was that of the pathogenic microorganisms. Koch, Pasteur, Ehrlich, and others acquainted the world with these self-reproducing and obviously living pathogens (disease carriers) and they gave us means, both physical and chemical, of combatting or removing them. People began to look hopefully toward a germ-free and disease-free future. But it soon became evident that there were many disease causing agents which did not obey all the rules laid down by the bacteriologists. In particular, many of these agents were found to pass through filters sufficiently fine to hold back even the smallest of the microorganisms, and they refused to increase and multiply in media which sufficed for even the most fastidious of these microorganisms. In these respects they resembled the simple poisons. However, when they entered a susceptible host and induced the disease, then they apparently multiplied readily. For, like the microorganisms, they could be serially transmitted through endless passages to innumerable hosts or victims. To this class of agents was given the name of filterable viruses and later, simply, viruses.

One early partial description of a virus we owe to Iwanowski. In 1892 this Russian investigator reported that the agent which produced the so-called mosaic disease of tobacco plants could be passed freely through bacterial filters. However, it remained for the Dutch bacteriologist Beijerinck to take, a few years later, the courageous mental step of recognizing that he was studying a new type of biological agent. In the following 30 years, through the work of many investigators, the biological status of the viruses became more clearly defined. Plants and animals were first found to harbor viruses, but it soon became evident that the bacteriophages discovered independently by Twort and d'Hérelle during World War I represented another class of viruses which were specially adapted to invade bacteria.

The next important advance, the study by Elford in 1931 in which the sizes of various viruses were deduced from their ability to pass graded porous membranes (sieves, so to speak), was generally disregarded because the time did not seem ripe for the acceptance of physical measurements for biological phenomena such as viruses. For viruses continued to be regarded as somewhat mysterious infectious agents, too small to be seen with the strongest microscopes or to be held back by filters. Further, they could not be cultured *in vitro* (in glass) but could be replicated only as they caused diseases in their hosts.

Thus, until the 1930's, virology seemed hardly the field to interest a chemist or even a biochemist, for these deal with material substances, not with mystic agents defined

	Diameter or width X length in mμ	General shape
Red blood cells	(7500)	
B. prodigiosus (Serratia marcescens)	750	
Rickettsia	475	
Psittacosis	270	
Myxoma	230 x 290	
Vaccinia	210 x 260	
Pleuro-pneumonia organism	150	
Herpes simplex	130	
Cytoplasmic virus (Tipula paludosa)	130	
Rabies fixe	125	
Newcastle disease	115	
Avian leucosis	120	
Vesicular stomatitis	65 x 165	
Polyhedral virus (Bombyx mori)	40 x 280	
Influenza	85	
Adeno	75	
Fowl plague	70	
T2 E. coli bacteriophage	65 x 95	
Chicken tumor I (Rous sarcoma)	65	
Equine encephalomyelitis	50	
T3 E. coli bacteriophage	45	
Rabbit papilloma (Shope)	45	
Tobacco mosaic and strains	15 x 300	
Cymbidium (orchid) mosaic	12 x 480	
Genetic unit (Muller's est of max. size)	20 x 125	
Southern bean mosaic	30	
Tomato bushy stunt	30	
Coxsackie	27	
Poliomyelitis	27	
Turnip yellow mosaic	26	
Tobacco ringspot	26	
Yellow fever	22	
Squash mosaic	22	
Hemocyanin molecule (Busycon)	22	
Foot-and-mouth disease	21	
Japanese B encephalitis	18	
Tobacco necrosis	16	
Hemoglobin molecule (Horse)	3 x 15	
Egg albumin molecule	2.5 x 10	

Fig. 1

almost entirely by negatives. The negative attitude was so prevalent that particles which had been seen with the microscope in cowpox fluid as early as 1887, and which were also found regularly in purified preparations of vaccinia virus, were called elementary bodies rather than virus particles, for were not viruses by definition invisible? In the same defeatist spirit, protein fractions carrying one or another virus activity, which were isolated about that time in several laboratories, were generally not identified with the virus. It needed another man with special scientific vision and courage to adopt a new working hypothesis: viruses can be regarded as big protein molecules, and the protein fraction highest in viral infectivity may actually represent the virus. This is the attitude which led Stanley in 1935 to describe the first isolation and crystallization of a virus, again the tobacco mosaic virus (TMV), which appears destined to mark so many of the milestones of the science of virology. With this discovery, or rather this proclamation of a new attitude, viruses became the subject of intensive chemical and physical research all over the world. It is a consequence of this development that the chemistry, physicochemistry, and biology of viruses now represents one of the most active fields of biochemical research and the subject matter for books, courses, and even radio and television programs.

In the light of present knowledge, typical viruses represent particles of a size ranging from that of small bacteria to that of big protein molecules (Fig. 1). They consist largely of protein which covers the other obligatory component, nucleic acid. Most viruses lack all enzymes, and none have metabolism. Upon entry into a competent living

---

Fig. 1. *Approximate sizes of viruses and reference objects. The red blood cell listed on top is not shown, since it is of ten times greater diameter (and 1000-fold weight) than the big bacterium shown. It will be noted that some viruses are bigger than the smallest bacteria (pleuro-pneumonia organism) and some are smaller than big protein molecules (hemocyanin), but most viruses fall between the two other groups. Nonviral reference objects are underlined.*

cell they can initiate a change in the metabolic pattern of that cell which leads to the production of virus nucleic acid and virus protein. Viruses thus elicit virus replication, but it is the cell that does the work and supplies the materials.

The impact of the recognition of the chemical and physical nature of viruses in the fields of public health, medicine, veterinary medicine, and plant pathology has been dramatic. However, the isolation of homogeneous particles endowed with genetic activity has had an even greater impact on biology as a whole. The study of pure viruses has stimulated the development of the new science of molecular biology which looks at biological processes, that is life, with the eyes of a chemist or physicist looking at molecules. Particularly the discovery that the nucleic acid of viruses alone is able to perform all crucial genetic functions has immensely broadened the basis of interest in viruses. For what we now learn about the chemistry of viruses and viral nucleic acids is closely linked to discoveries and conclusions concerning normal and pathological cellular particles and cellular genetic material. The fields of biochemistry, biophysics, genetics, oncology, cytology, and virology are fusing in the general area of molecular biology, and the chemically purified viruses represent one of its most convenient and fruitful objects of study.

The estimation and isolation of plant viruses

THE CHEMICAL STUDY OF biological materials such as viruses, hormones, and enzymes begins in earnest only after these have been isolated in pure form, free from other cellular components. Such isolation is usually a difficult procedure. It is greatly facilitated if a convenient and quantitative biological test is available. For then one can detect the presence of the active component and measure its enrichment in the course of its separation from other inactive materials. Many viruses can be estimated by comparatively simple and accurate bioassays, and such viruses are usually selected for detailed biochemical study. Plant viruses which belong in this class are the ones which give so-called local lesions, usually small discolored spots indicative of diseased tissue on the inoculated leaf surface. The number of such spots per leaf is roughly proportional to the virus concentration of the inoculum. Frequently one-half of a leaf receives a solution of unknown virus content, and the other a known or "standard" virus solution. From the ratio of lesions appearing on the two halves, the virus concentration in the unknown solution can be calculated. Further, inspection of Fig. 2 * shows spots of very different size on the two halves of a tobacco leaf. These are produced by two different strains or variants of tobacco mosaic virus. We will say

* See figures at end of book.

9

much more about strains later; this photo serves to illustrate that it can be as easy to tell strains apart from the appearance of lesions as to determine their relative concentration from the number of lesions per half leaf.

For the isolation of a virus, one wants it to be present in the host tissue in the highest possible concentration. One can determine that concentration by grinding up a little of the infected tissue and applying test samples to a local lesion host. If one does that with TMV and other plant viruses, one finds that plant varieties which respond with local lesions are not very rich in virus per leaf, or per plant. Other varieties, for instance, Turkish tobacco, permit the virus to spread freely throughout the plant, and it is in these varieties that one can usually find the highest concentrations of virus in the press juice. Thus TMV, when rubbed onto one or two leaves of a small Turkish tobacco plant, a variety on which it does not give local lesions, will increase in concentration and spread throughout the rapidly growing plant, so that after 3 weeks one may end up with a 20-fold bigger plant containing millions of times as much virus as was used for the inoculum.

This description of virus propagation gives the impression that the virus does not harm the plant. Actually, typical TMV causes some decrease in the growth rate of Turkish tobacco, as well as distortion of the leaves, a mosaic pattern of discoloration, and other symptoms. Other variants or strains of the virus show more severe effects and may gradually kill the plant. Others are milder, and some strains are known to grow well on Turkish tobacco without causing any visible symptom on that host. Some other plant and animal viruses have similarly friendly relations to their host, resembling the symbiotic relationship between certain higher organisms. Even more extraordinary, but outside the scope of this little book, is the state of lysogeny, which means that certain bacterial viruses can for endless bacterial generations entirely merge with the genetic matter of the microorganism, becoming completely undetectable until their autonomous replication is artificially provoked by ultraviolet light (UV) or certain chemicals.

This brief excursion into the biology of viruses comes to an end. Our concern here is not with the disease, or the lack of a disease, but with the production of viruses for further study. Since viruses do not grow in soil but only in living cells, our virus field, at least for the procurement of TMV, is a tobacco patch. A variety of methods have been used to get the virus out of the plant tissue, and only the principles of those most frequently employed will be mentioned. One usually first freezes the plants, since that makes them easier to grind up into a pulp. Often it is of advantage to do this grinding in the presence of added sodium phosphate buffer salts to keep the plant acids neutralized. One then squeezes the juice through cheese cloth or other coarse filters to free it from insoluble plant material.

The main principle employed in getting viruses out of such plant juices takes advantage of their physical properties as particles bigger than most other molecules and yet smaller than cell walls and membranes and globs of denatured proteins. These principles will become clearer when we discuss the properties of proteins in a later chapter. The procedure is to centrifuge the juice at a comparatively slow speed, about 10,000 rpm, faster than ordinary laboratory centrifuges but not fast enough to pack the virus particles together at the bottom of the tube. Under these conditions much of the debris, including the chlorophyll carrying particles of plant cells, the so-called chloroplasts, are packed together. The supernatant fluid is then centrifuged in an ultracentrifuge at 20,000–30,000 rpm, which gives a centrifugal field about 62,000 times stronger than gravity and results in the sedimentation of typical viruses in the form of gels at the bottom of the tube. The supernate containing all small-molecular plant components, such as sugars, salts, soluble proteins, and free chlorophyll, is discarded. The sediment, usually referred to as a pellet, can be redispersed in water or salt solutions with patience and a bit of gentle

DRAKE MEMORIAL LIBRARY
STATE UNIVERSITY COLLEGE
BROCKPORT, NEW YORK

stirring or shaking. If the virus concentration is appreciable (e.g., about 10 mg per ml), the solution will not look water-clear, for virus particles are big enough to scatter light and thus give the solution an opalescent appearance. For further purification, the same procedure is repeated several times: low speed centrifugation to remove big debris, and high speed centrifugation to sediment the virus and remove small-molecular materials. When the pellet has a colorless and translucent appearance, it is probably composed entirely of virus particles, and the isolation of the virus has been accomplished successfully.

At times, this technique of differential centrifugation is inadequate to free virus from other materials, and different principles must be invoked. The method of density gradient centrifugation, in which the virus is centrifuged in a solution of salt or sugar increasing in concentration from top to bottom, separates the virus from materials of different density. Since nucleic acids have a higher density than most other cellular components, and viruses are nucleoproteins containing a definite amount of nucleic acid, this technique is quite selective. Other methods take advantage of the fact that the contaminating proteins are often more easily denatured and rendered insoluble than the virus particle. This can be achieved by heating under carefully controlled conditions, or by treatment with ethyl alcohol, or with solvents such as butanol, which are not miscible with water. The separation of viruses is also possible by the standard methods of protein chemistry, such as stepwise salting out of virus and other proteins by the addition of more and more ammonium sulfate. This method was the first to lead to pure TMV in the hands of Dr. Stanley in 1935, but it has now been largely replaced by the method of differential centrifugation. By such methods, singly or in combination, at least 50 different plant viruses or strains have been purified and subjected to chemical study. Many of them form beautiful crystals indistinguishable in shape and regularity from those of simple compounds, such as sugars or salts.

The isolation of animal and bacterial viruses

THE PURIFICATION OF ANImal and bacterial viruses, in general, relies on the same principles as those of the plant viruses. Animal viruses frequently do not reach very high concentrations in the tissue. In addition to this, the amounts of cellular proteins present is considerably higher in animal than in plant cells. All this makes the isolation of animal viruses much more difficult, and relatively few animal viruses have therefore been purified.

The two animal viruses on which most chemical work has been done are the influenza virus and the poliomyelitis virus. The isolation of the influenza and related viruses is greatly facilitated by their specific tendency to become adsorbed onto red bloods cells. Polio virus owes much of its intensive study to having found an illustrious host in F. D. Roosevelt. The isolation of the polio virus was one of the first instances where a butanol two-phase system was applied successfully in virus purification. Also of great advantage here has been the use of enzymes, which makes use of the fact that viruses are generally much more resistant to attack by enzymes than are other cellular components. More recently, poliomyelitis virus has also become the first animal virus to be crystallized. It must be noted, however, that crystallization of particles as big as viruses, while esthetically satisfying, does not necessarily mean a higher level of purity or infectivity than that characteristic of the amorphous form (Fig. 3C, D*). Recently a new chromatographic method for the isolation of great amounts of polio virus has been described. Yet, great amounts of an animal virus represent only a matter of a few mg, while plant viruses are prepared in gram-amounts (1 ounce $= 28$ g $= 28,000$ mg).

The isolation of bacteriophages relies mostly on the principle of differential centrifugation, although differential filtration and precipitation methods are also occasionally used. A group of quite similar RNA-containing bacteriophages has become available for study in recent years. It is comparatively easy to obtain appreciable amounts of these by a combination of standard methods (ammonium sulfate precipitation, and both differential and gradient centrifugation) as well as one step of emulsifying the tissue in a mixture of water and a chlorinated hydrocarbon which causes denaturation of most proteins but leaves the virus intact in the aqueous phase.

We have previously stressed the importance of a good bioassay for any research on biologically active materials. This condition is very well fulfilled in the case of the bacteriophages, since each phage particle with its progeny eats a distinct and easily countable hole in a carpet of bacteria. Many animal viruses can now be quantitatively determined with similar ease, thanks to the development of tissue culture techniques.

* See figures at end of book.

The architecture
of virus particles

THE PRESENT METHODS OF isolation of viruses usually rely on, or at least include, differential centrifugation. This means that all particles within a certain range of size and weight are separated from coarser cell debris and protein precipitates on the one hand, and from soluble proteins and small molecular compounds and salts on the other. Various physicochemical tests can be applied to determine the state of uniformity or homogeneity of the resulting virus preparation. Quantitative assays of the infectivity will also serve to tell the experimenter when his preparation consists largely of infective virus particles. He will then usually want to "look at" his particles, and electron microscopy now enables him to do so. If the virus that is being purified has a characteristic shape, such as the TMV particle or many bacteriophages (see Fig. 3), then one good electron micrograph will show whether the bulk of the material in the preparation is accounted for by the characteristic particles, or if appreciable amounts of other noncharacteristic particulate matter is still present. If the virus is roughly spherical, then this differentiation is often not so easy, since spherical particles can be isolated from most biological material, whether it is infected with a virus or not. The tendency of such particles to arrange themselves in beautifully regular or crystalline arrays (see Fig. 3) can be regarded as indicative of

15

their chemical uniformity and viral nature. Assuming that the observed particles actually represent a virus, the next question is: How is it built up, and what gives it its shape?

A variety of methods are used to ascertain the internal architecture of a purified virus. Electron microscopy of particles which have been partially degraded or disrupted can be most illustrative. X-ray diffraction analysis has proven an even more powerful tool. This is a technique in which X-rays are permitted to pass through the material. If the atoms are aligned in an orderly (e.g., crystalline) pattern, then the X-rays will be diffracted in an orderly manner, and from the angle of scattering the atomic arrangement can be deduced by the experts. Finally, the accessibility of the various viral components to chemical agents or enzymes can tell us much about their spatial arrangement. From the sum total of these and other studies, it has become abundantly clear that in the simple viruses each particle consists of many comparatively small protein molecules of one or occasionally two types covering one long coiled-up nucleic acid molecule. The relative arrangement of these two viral components in TMV, and probably in other long rod-like particles, is well illustrated in Fig. 4.* This model was constructed by the English X-ray analytical team headed by Rosalind Franklin, who elucidated many of the structural features of TMV. The model was exhibited at the world exposition in Brussels in 1958. No other virus is known in similar detail. However, the ribonucleic acid (RNA) of spherical viruses is surely also located internally and covered by small (roughly spherical) protein subunits. This relationship is illustrated by the fact that protein particles which have frequently been observed in infected material show identical dimensions and surface properties to the respective virus but lack the nucleic acid and are noninfectious. More about these particles later. Their existence and their properties definitely show that the external coat of the corresponding virus is protein in nature.

Whenever one considers structural aspects of biological

* See figures at end of book.

material, be it the gross anatomy of man or the molecular arrangements of a virus particle, a simultaneous consideration of the functional aspects is of great advantage. Structure is a product of evolution, and the functional perfection of a given structure often represents its evolutionary password. We will therefore now consider virus structure in relation to virus function. This will be done in quite cursory manner, for we will again return to this subject in a later chapter.

Most of our knowledge in this field is of relatively recent origin and, as yet, quite fragmentary. Some of the current concepts may change as new data become available, or new interpretations become necessary. All a scientist can do is to hope that his conclusions are not too far from the truth. Yet if they are generally and unquestioningly accepted, and particularly if they are treated as religious dogma which nobody dares or cares to contradict, then a true scientist feels all the more constrained to doubt them and to investigate new lines of evidence.

The typical particles representing simple viruses are now regarded as transport forms of the infective agent. As will later be demonstrated, the infective agent is the RNA, a single long-chain molecule. In some manner, this molecule is released from its protein coat upon entry into the host cell, possibly in the nucleus of the cell. The RNA then initiates the production of replicas of itself, be it through the intermediacy of new enzymes or directly. Somewhat later it initiates the production of its coat protein in the form of the relatively small peptide chains. This probably occurs largely in the body of the cell, the so-called cytoplasm, while the RNA may be made in the nucleus. The RNA then leaves the nucleus and in the cytoplasm combines with the virus protein, which all by itself has a great tendency to aggregate in a specific manner but does so even more readily with and around the RNA. Thus the new virus particles are formed. This process, which represents a sort of co-crystallization of two compatible molecular species, takes place automatically and even *in vitro* (in a test tube) under suitable conditions (see later). Thus, the shape of the virus is entirely dictated by the shape and clumping affinities of the protein. This is particularly well illustrated by the natural occurrence of the previously mentioned particles composed only of protein. However, such nucleic-acid-free particles are obviously not functional. Furthermore, they are generally much more labile than the virus. And here we come to the heart of the matter: complete virus particles are remarkably more stable than either of their components alone. This is probably of greatest functional importance as far as the nucleic acid is concerned. For nucleic acids are very susceptible to attack by various enzymes (so-called nucleases and phosphatases) which abound in the cytoplasm; but they are completely resistant to these enzymes when encased in their protein. Thus the protein coat may be of greatest importance for the spreading and transmission of viruses.

The complete particle must also be able to withstand other potentially harmful agents, such as the protein splitting (proteolytic) enzymes and heat. And it is an additional remarkable feature of the coaggregation of much protein with less RNA that not only the RNA, but also the protein, is greatly stabilized and protected as a result of aggregation. Thus, function demands, and the structure assures, that the RNA of viruses be completely covered by a very stable protein shell and that that protein shell may nevertheless be assembled and disassembled with relative ease. We will now proceed to a brief discussion of the chemical nature of proteins and nucleic acid in general and those of certain viruses in particular. After that, we will be in a better position to understand the experimental basis for the conclusions stated in this section.

The chemical structure
of proteins

LIVING MATTER CONSISTS
mainly of proteins, and life, as we know it, is largely the
consequence of a series of protein reactions. The chemical
nature and reactivity of proteins is, therefore, one of the
key problems of biology. One important biological function, the preservation and transmission of the blueprints
of heredity, is carried by nucleic acids, but these genetically
active nucleic acids are usually associated with proteins
which contribute to their function in various ways. This
is also true for the viruses. The protein of a virus often
represents one of its most accessible and characteristic
features. Historically, virus chemistry started as a branch
of protein chemistry. Thus, Stanley isolated the first virus
and demonstrated its chemical purity by the methods of
protein isolation and protein characterization; significantly,
he shared the Nobel prize with Northrop and Sumner, the
crystallizers of the protein enzymes pepsin, trypsin, and
urease. These facts have been presented in the hope that
they might elicit in the reader some curiosity and interest
concerning the principles of protein chemistry, which represents the subject matter of this chapter.

Proteins are polymers formed through condensation of
amino acids. Typical amino acids, conforming properly to
the nomenclature, carry an amino ($-NH_2$) and a carboxylic
acid ($-COOH$) group:

19

$$\begin{array}{ccc} H & R & O \\ \diagdown & | & \diagup \\ & N{-}C{-}C \\ \diagup & | & \diagdown \\ H & H & O{-}H \end{array}$$

[To refresh the reader's memory of the principles of organic chemistry: carbon (C) usually has four bonds; nitrogen (N), three; oxygen (O), two; and hydrogen (H), one. The nature of the R group will be explained later. Ionized forms may have one bond more or less and, therefore, carry a positive or negative charge.] Condensation, in organic chemistry, means a coupling of two molecules with loss of one molecule of water, and it is evident that long chain molecules can be obtained by this reaction from the ambidextrous amino acids. The condensation of four amino acids is illustrated in Scheme 1, with the so-called amino acid residues, i.e., the amino acids lacking the elements of water (—NH—CHR—CO—), enclosed in arrows with bulges for the R groups of varying sizes (see later).

In the process of condensation, each amino acid loses its most outspoken chemical characteristics, its acidic and its basic group; it sacrifices these to a new chemical principle which contributes importantly to the nature of proteins, the peptide bond, —CO—NH—. The condensation of 4 amino acid molecules yields a so-called tetrapeptide, as shown in Scheme 1. Although no sharp dividing line exists between peptides and proteins, molecules containing fewer than 50 amino acid residues are usually referred to as polypeptides, and those containing more numerous residues, as proteins. Proteins owe many of their properties to the fact that they are big molecules. The study of synthetic high polymers is only about 50 years old, but the fact that our time has been termed the age of plastics is an illustration of the rapid development and the multitudinous practical applications of this field of high polymer chemistry. Research along these lines has also yielded an understanding of the forces governing the interactions of high polymers and giving them their desired physical properties. In principle these forces are neither new nor different from those affect-

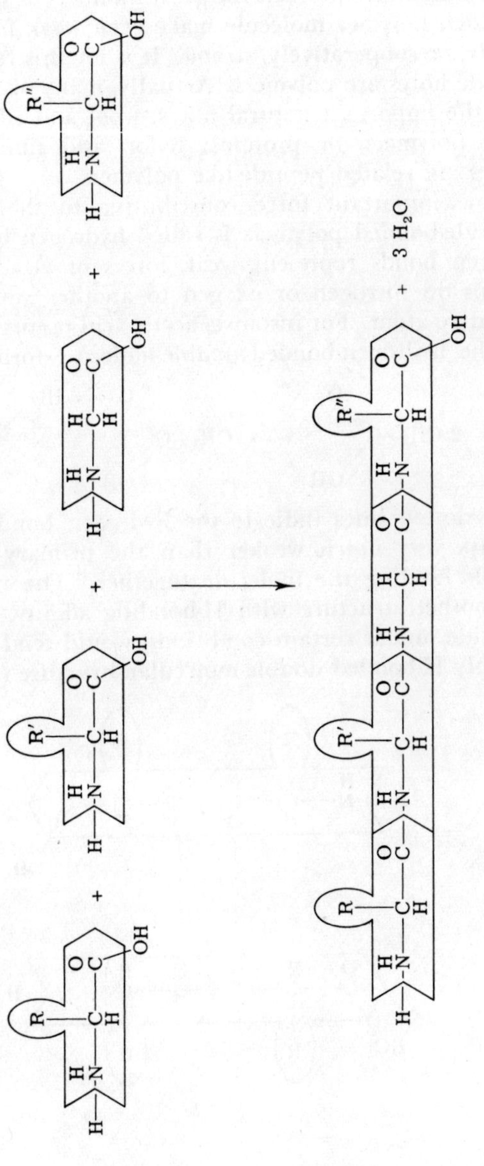

SCHEME 1

ing small molecules, but the great numbers of similar groups on each polymer molecule make even weak forces cumulatively, or cooperatively, strong. It is for this reason that all textile fibres are polymers. Actually, many of them, including the important natural fibres, wool and silk, are amino acid polymers, or proteins; nylon and similar synthetic fibres are related peptide-like polymers.

One important force contributing to the structure of peptide-bonded polymers is called hydrogen bonding. Hydrogen bonds represent weak forces of attachment of H atoms on nitrogen or oxygen to another similar, electronegative atom. For instance, acetic acid occurs in good part in the hydrogen-bonded double-molecule form:

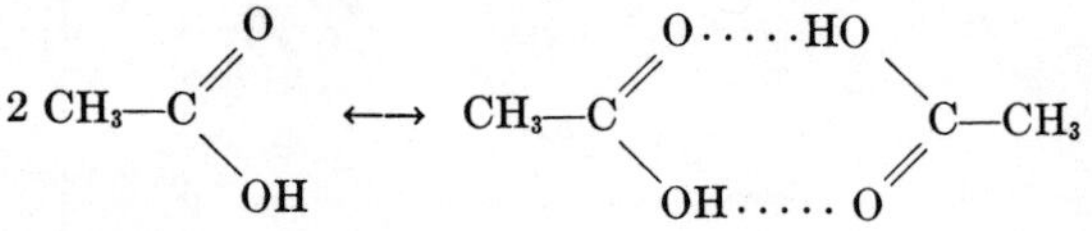

The dotted lines indicate the hydrogen bonds, which are always very much weaker than the primary inter-atomic bonds holding the molecule together. The peptide bond is another structure with H-bonding affinity. Thus, a dipeptide, under certain conditions, would tend to form this doubly H-bonded double-molecular structure (I).

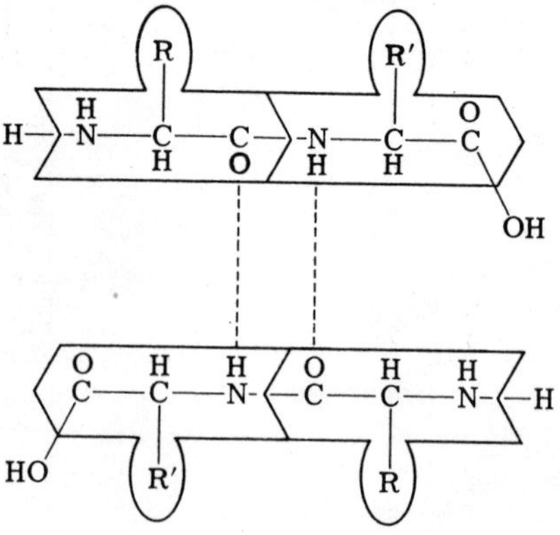

I

As stated above, the cumulative strength of the great number of such bonds, even though individually weak, is very high in long chain polypeptides such as proteins. It gives proteins definite physical properties of great importance. A few examples of the biological role of H-bonds are the strength of tendons and ligaments, as well as of hair and wool, the clotting of blood, and the antibody reactions which protect us from disease. However, bonding does not only occur between chains (inter-chain) but also often between peptide bonds on the same chain [intra-chain (Fig. 5A)]. One important internal structural arrangement frequently occurring in synthetic polypeptides, and probably also in proteins, has been defined by Pauling as the α-helix. This term describes a peptide chain folded into a helical path (Fig. 5B) with about 3 residues in each turn, an arrangement which favors H-bonding between peptide linkages from one turn of the screw to the next. Other means of peptide chain folding probably also exist. The most stable proteins will be those in which the greatest proportion of the potentially hydrogen-bonding sites are linked to a suitable partner.

Let us now consider what will happen when we heat a solution of an intra-chain bonded, and thus well-rounded, so-called globular or native protein, such as the ovalbumin of egg white. Heat increases the Brownian motion of the molecules; they get "shook up." A few of the weaker hydrogen bonds, probably near chain ends, begin to break, thus further weakening the structure. Soon, more and more molecules will ever faster uncurl, and this process will continue until nothing remains but long thread-like chains studded with available peptide bonds; these in turn tend to couple with complete promiscuity with others (randomness is the scientific term) often located on other chains. The final result will be an irregular network of peptide chain fibres with most of the protein forming one enormous aggregate molecule, often a gel. This general process is called denaturation, and our specific product is a hard-boiled egg.

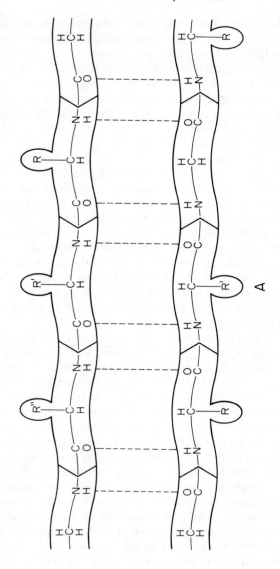

Fɪɢ. 5. *A. Schematic representation of hydrogen bond interaction be-*
tween peptide bonds (—CO———HN—), shown here between two
peptide chains.

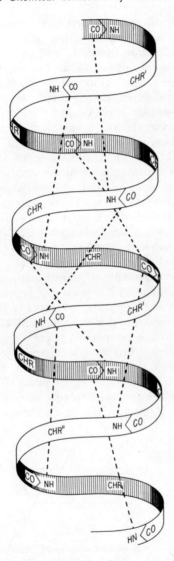

FIG. 5. *B. Hydrogen bond interaction between turns of a screw-like (α-helix) arrangement of a single peptide chain. The structural units in both cases are amino acid residues (—NH—CHR—CO—) in which R, R', R'', etc., represent side chains of varying complexity (see p. 27).*

We have until now focused our attention on the high polymer aspects of proteins or polypeptides. Proteins, however, are much more complex, and thus more interesting, than most other polymers, natural or synthetic. This is so because proteins are composed of many different amino acids carrying different chemical residues on the carbon between each peptide bond, as indicated by the symbols **R**, **R′**, **R″**, etc., and drawn in varying sizes in our schematic formulas. Thus, proteins are polymers of usually about 20 different building blocks, and most of the properties of proteins are the consequence of the particular arrangement of amino acid residues, and thus of **R** groups, along the chain. The polymer chemist thinks only in statistical terms about his materials, which are mixtures of molecules of different length and, if he deals with a copolymer (more than one component), of different sequence. In contrast, all molecules of a given protein are probably alike in number and sequential arrangement of amino acids along the chain. This is of fundamental importance, because the **R** groups of the amino acids residues vary greatly in their chemical nature and thus can produce different chemical environments in different segments of a peptide chain. To illustrate this, and facilitate further understanding, I will now give a list and brief characterization of the **R** groups of the typical amino acids occurring in proteins. All except the last two have the general structure shown in (II) with the nature of the **R** group defining its chemical character.

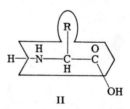

II

A brief discussion of the chemical attributes given in the last column of this table is in order. The most pronounced characteristic of amino acids is their dipolar nature. Actu-

NATURE OF THE R GROUP

R	Name of amino acid and abbreviation	Characteristics
—H	glycine (gly)	none (lacks asymetric C atom which makes all other amino acids optically active)
—CH₃	alanine (ala)	none
$-CH \begin{smallmatrix} CH_3 \\ CH_3 \end{smallmatrix}$	valine (val)	aliphatic (hydrophobic, affinity for fat solvents, detergents, etc.)
$-CH_2-CH \begin{smallmatrix} CH_3 \\ CH_3 \end{smallmatrix}$	leucine (leu)	aliphatic (hydrophobic, affinity for fat solvents, detergents, etc.)
$-CH \begin{smallmatrix} CH_3 \\ \end{smallmatrix} -CH_2-CH_3$	isoleucine (ileu)	aliphatic (hydrophobic, affinity for fat solvents, detergents, etc.)
—CH₂OH	serine (ser)	hydrophilic (occurs in active site of many enzymes)
—CHOH—CH₃	threonine (thr)	hydrophilic
—CH₂—COOH	aspartic acid (asp)	acidic, hydrophilic
—CH₂—CH₂—COOH	glutamic acid (glu)	acidic, hydrophilic
—CH₂—CONH₂	asparagine (aspNH₂)	none

NATURE OF THE R GROUP (continued)

Structure	Name	Nature
—CH₂—CH₂—CONH₂	glutamine (gluNH₂)	none
—CH₂—CH₂—CH₂—CH₂NH₂	lysine (lys)	basic, hydrophilic
—CH₂—CH₂—CH₂—NH—C(=NH)NH₂	arginine (arg)	very basic, hydrophilic
(imidazole ring)	histidine (his)	weakly basic (important for enzyme activities)
(benzene ring)	phenylalanine (phe)	aromatic, hydrophobic
(phenol ring, —C—OH)	tyrosine (tyr)	aromatic, UV light absorbing
(indole ring)	tryptophan (try)	aromatic, UV light absorbing

Structure	Name	Description
—CH₂—SH	cysteine (cySH)	oxidizable (important for many enzymes)
—CH₂—S —CH₂—S	cystine (cyS—Scy)	structurally important because it forms bridges between peptides, being attached to 2 amino and carboxyl groups
—CH₂—CH₂—S—CH₃	methionine (met)	oxidizable
$$\begin{array}{c} CH_2-CH_2 \\ | \qquad | \\ H-N \qquad CH-CH_2 \\ \qquad\quad | \\ \qquad\quad COOH \end{array}$$	proline (pro)	In these the R group forms a ring involving the peptide N, thus changing the nature of that peptide bond. The entire amino acid is represented
$$\begin{array}{c} CH_2-CHOH \\ | \qquad | \\ H-N \qquad CH-CH_2 \\ \qquad\quad | \\ \qquad\quad COOH \end{array}$$	hydroxyproline	

ally, they represent internal salts in neutral aqueous solution, so-called zwitter ions, because their carboxyl groups give off a hydrogen ion or proton and their amino groups bind a proton under such conditions. It is the resultant negative charge on the carboxyl group that makes it acidic and the positive charge on the amino groups that makes it basic.

$$\left(\begin{array}{c} \text{H}_2\text{N—CH—COOH} \\ | \\ \text{R} \end{array} \right) \rightarrow$$

In neutral solution:

$$\text{H}_3\text{N}^+\text{—CH—COO}^- \atop | \atop \text{R}$$

In acid solution: $\text{H}_3\text{N}^+\text{—CHR—COOH}$

In basic solution: $\text{H}_2\text{N—CHR—COO}^-$

As previously stated, the formation of peptide bonds abolishes these polar characteristics of the component amino acids. There remain, however, the chain end groups which, under physiological conditions of neutral pH, are not H$_2$N—, and —COOH, as shown on p. 21, but actually H$_3$N$^+$—, and —COO$^-$. And the same is true for the acidic and basic R groups listed above. The guanidinium group of arginine is so strongly basic that under all circumstances in water solution it carries an extra hydrogen ion (proton) which flits from one of the 3 nitrogens to the other, thus frustrating its graphical presentation

$$\text{—NH—C}^+ \begin{array}{c} \overset{\textcircled{H}}{} \quad \text{NH}_2 \\ \\ \text{NH} \end{array}$$

The imidazole groups of histidine picks up a proton at just about neutral pH

$$\begin{array}{c} \text{—C—NH} \\ \| \quad \diagdown \\ \quad \quad \text{CH} \\ \| \quad \diagup \\ \text{CH—N} \end{array} \xrightarrow{+\text{H}^+} \begin{array}{c} \text{—C—NH}_2^+ \\ \| \quad \diagdown \\ \quad \quad \text{CH} \\ \| \quad \diagup \\ \text{CH—N} \end{array}$$

The others (lysine, glutamic and aspartic acid) are usually ionized under such conditions (H_3N^+—, —COO^-).

These charges represent hooks with which the protein molecules can grab ions of opposite charge. Thus, in water containing a salt, let us say sodium chloride, the chloride ions (Cl^-) will hover near the ammonium groups (—NH_3^+), while the sodium ions (Na^+) will be attracted by the carboxylate groups (—COO^-). However, the neighboring amino acid residues of any such protein group can influence its affinity, so that it may bind certain ions much more readily than others. Thus, we begin to understand the advantages of the macromolecular state as a means of forming specific or selective areas on the surface of a protein. The simplest illustration is the binding of a divalent metal ion, let us say calcium (Ca^{++}). Such a divalent ion will be caught by two adjacent —COO^- groups and thus become much more firmly fixed at such a site than the sodium ions, which, consequently, would be knocked off by calcium, if they were there first.

Now we proceed to the discussion of hydrophobic and hydrophilic groups. Hydrophobic, water-fearing, is a property of hydrocarbons, compounds composed mostly, if not entirely, of C and H atoms, such as benzene

$$
\begin{array}{c}
HC\!\!-\!\!CH \\
HC \diagup \quad \diagdown CH \\
HC\!\!=\!\!CH
\end{array}
$$

or gasoline,

CH_3—CH_2—CH_2—CH_2—CH_2—CH_2—CH_2—CH_3 (normal octane).

These liquids are not miscible with water but are good solvents for one another and for most other compounds of similar nature. Evidently, certain of the R groups in our table, such as those of leucine and phenylalanine, belong to this class. The protein as a whole likes water, or is hydrophilic, since most of its R groups are either ionized or contain —OH groups with varying affinities for water. Even the ubiquitous peptide bond and the amide groups

(—$CONH_2$) have a tendency to bind water by hydrogen bonding. Thus, if we add a hydrophobic compound to a protein solution, the two will not find it easy to become acquainted and will usually stay apart. Let us, however, add to the protein an hydrophobic compound carrying an ionized group, for instance, $CH_3(CH_2)_{16}$—COO^-Na^+ (sodium stearate, which is one of the main components of soap) and this compound will, owing to its —COO^- group, become attracted to an —NH_3^+ group of the protein. The long hydrophobic chain will readily find birds of a feather in the leucine and valine residues in the vicinity on the protein chain and will become multiply attached. In the process, the fatty acid molecule displaces, we hope, any less firmly attached and often colored compounds which we call dirt, and then the experiment is a success. Again you see that protein reactions frequently involve more than one group, and here, as in most cases, more than one type of group participates in the reaction.

We have given as examples two very simple and general protein reactions, the binding of a divalent ion, and of a fatty acid or detergent. The difference between these effects and the enzymatic action of proteins, which encompass about half of the "Secret-of-Life," is probably one only of degree of complexity and sophistication. We know a protein, conalbumin of egg white, which seems to exist only for the purpose of binding iron so firmly that it is almost impossible to displace it. About 350 amino acid residues are curled into a particular shape to create a niche with a remarkable fit for, and hold on, one iron atom (Fe^{+++}). We know another protein in egg white, avidin, that binds with equal or even greater selectivity the vitamin biotin, removing it from solution down to the last traces so that bacteria, even though they require only extremely small traces of the vitamin, cannot survive in the presence of this avid protein. In these and similar cases nothing but protein binding affinities are involved, and these are not principally different from those leading to the binding of calcium or soap.

Let us now proceed to a consideration of the mechanism of enzyme action. Most proteins are enzymes, and enzymes are the agents which make and break all cellular components and supply the energy and the know-how to keep the intricate cellular machinery working smoothly and efficiently. How do enzymes work? Well, it seems well established that specific sites on the surface of the enzyme proteins bind the substrate, the compound to be chemically altered, in a selective manner similar to the examples given above. In this embrace, the substrate weakens, and either through the action of helper molecules, so-called co-enzymes, that are bound in the vicinity, or only through the strain of the peptide chain that it is doubly or triply attached to, the substrate undergoes the necessary change. The complete and detailed mechanism is not yet known for the action of any enzyme, but with several of them the scientific detectives are getting close to their goal of reconstructing the crime. There is no question that the main agent of enzyme function is the structure of the specific protein.

Protein structure is a double problem. First one must unravel what is called the primary structure, which means the number of peptide chains (for there can be several, see Figs. 5A, 6) and the number and arrangement of the amino acids along each chain. And then one must determine the arrangement of the chain or chains in space, the folding and curling which gives the molecule a definite shape, which brings distant R groups close together, and which may make the protein biologically active. Methods are now available to solve the first problem, the establishment of the number of chains and their amino acid composition and sequence, although the elucidation of the sequence is still a formidably complicated and exacting task for big proteins containing hundreds of amino acid residues. For the second problem, the nature of the folding, chemical techniques are only in the early stages of experimentation, but it appears that recent refinements in the technique and study of X-ray scattering diagrams (see p. 16) may make this a most powerful

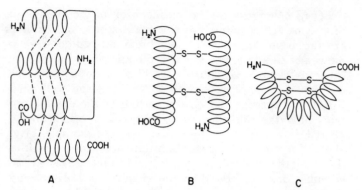

A   B   C

Fig. 6. *Schematic presentation of three types of protein chain arrangement. All chains are assumed to be largely helical, which is not necessarily so. A. A two-chain molecule held together only by secondary forces (the principle of the structure of hemoglobin). B. A two-chain protein held together only by the sulfur atoms of the double amino acid cystine (the principle of the structure in insulin). C. A single-chain cystine crosslinked molecule (the principle holding for ribonuclease and lysozyme). See also Fig. 7 for a more detailed presentation of this structure.*

It must be stressed that these drawings represent serious oversimplifications and that usually more than one type of bonding will occur between the peptide chains of any given protein, though to a varying extent.

tool for the purpose of determining the three-dimensional structure of proteins. It should also be noted that the so-called secondary structure of proteins, the three-dimensional folding, appears unimportant or nonexistent for some types of biological activity, such as that of certain protein hormones. But the viral coat proteins, like the enzymes, have this added complexity of structure.

Having outlined the two-fold aspect of protein structure, we will now proceed to a description of the present techniques of amino acid analysis and the methods for unravelling the amino acid sequences of proteins. Analysis of the amino acid composition of the protein under study is usually performed first and referred back to in the course of solving the jigsaw puzzle of the allocation of amino acids along the chain. Boiling the protein in strong acid breaks all peptide bonds and permits the separation of the resultant amino acids. At present, the separation and determination of amino acids can be achieved overnight by an automatic machine with considerable accuracy, if all goes well. One amino acid, tryptophan, is destroyed by acid and must be separately determined; certain others are slowly decomposed with prolonged boiling with acid, while again others are only slowly released from peptide linkage. Thus, different time periods of hydrolysis are usually used, and the final decision as to whether there are 12 or 13 serines and 15 or 16 leucines in a 200 residue protein requires judgment and is therefore subject to error. Methods of analysis, other than the automatic, are useful and quite adequate for peptides and small proteins, but they are also quite laborious and time consuming.

The crucial discovery which stimulated the rapid development of the field of sequence analysis was a method designed by Sanger in 1945 for the labelling of the so-called N-terminal (H_2N—CHR—CO—) residue by means of fluorodinitrobenzene, a reagent which makes the terminal amino acid yellow (Scheme 2). This procedure made it possible to detect and identify the terminal residue with relative ease,

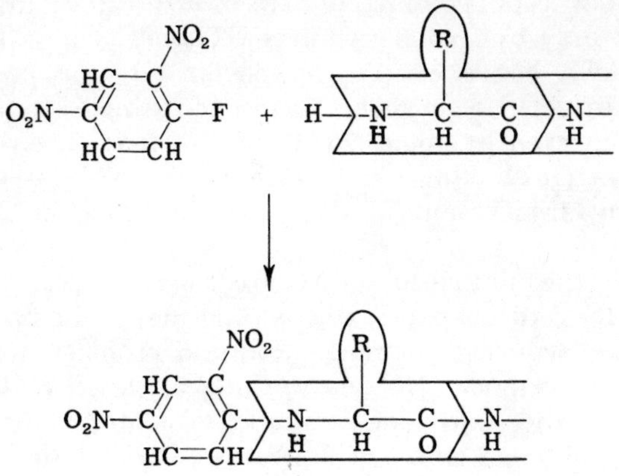

SCHEME 2

after hydrolysis of the protein. Other methods followed which permitted stepwise degradation, splitting off one amino acid after another from the N-terminus. Two types of enzymes (aminopeptidase and carboxypeptidases) were also found to be useful tools, since they attacked a peptide chain starting with either the N-terminal (NH_2—CHR—CO——) or the C-terminal (——NH—CHR—COOH) residue and progressively released one residue at a time (at least in principle). Chemical methods of identifying the C-terminal amino acid were also discovered. These end-group methods first supplied information concerning the number and nature of chains. If the protein under study consisted of more than one chain, then these had to be separated before any sequence study could be attempted. Thus insulin, the first protein to be subjected to this kind of study by Sanger, proved to have in one molecule (51 amino acids) two N-terminal residues (glycine, phenylalanine) and two C-terminal residues (asparagine, alanine) and was thus composed of two chains (20 and 31 residues long, respectively). These were held together by the —S—S— bridges of the double amino acid, cystine (see Fig. 6). After these —S—S— bridges had been broken by oxidation, the two chains could be separated and then separately subjected to analysis. Hemoglobin consists of two different pairs of identical chains held together only by secondary forces (H-bonds, salt linkages, hydrophobic bonds; see Fig. 6). So far, all virus proteins studied in detail seem to be, fortunately, single-chain proteins. But even in single chain proteins it is necessary to break any crosslinking bonds, such as the —S—S— bonds shown in Figs. 6C and 7, before structural analysis is possible.

While the described procedures may appear quite straight-forward on paper, this is often not so in practice, for certain sequences represent technical problems for several or all methods. Nobody working in this field would dare to predict how long it would take him to unravel the order of 6 or 8 amino acids. But we were talking about proteins, and a small protein such as the coat protein of

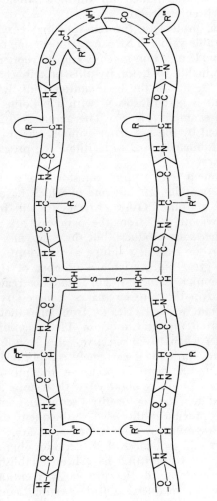

FIG. 7. Schematic presentation of a peptide chain loop showing one crosslinking cystine residue and a pair of interacting R″ residues, e.g., two leucine residues. If the perfectionist reader is concerned about the unequal length of the amino acid residues (—NH—CH—CO), he may view the drawing as three-dimensional and accept shorter residues as foreshortened.

TMV consists of a single chain of 158 amino acids. Obviously, the methods mentioned up till now would be inadequate for such chain lengths.

In this dilemma, proteolytic (protein-splitting) enzymes proved of considerable value. The pancreatic enzyme trypsin (about whose mode of action much is known) represents a particularly invaluable tool, for it splits protein chains selectively on the "right" of the basic amino acids, lysine and arginine. This is best illustrated with a hypothetical peptide serving as example (Fig. 8). The amino acid residues are represented by the 3–4 letter symbols (see list on pp. 27–29) now customarily used to facilitate the presentation of long sequences.

As shown, treatment with trypsin transforms a protein into a number of peptides, all but one of which have C-terminal lysine or arginine. Other enzymes (pepsin from the stomach or chymotrypsin from the pancreas) are also used and yield other split products, but these enzymes are not as selective for one class of residues, as is trypsin, and thus produce too great and variable a number of short peptides to be of similar usefulness. For it must be remembered that the enzymatic splitting makes it necessary to separate the resultant peptides cleanly from one another before their sequential analysis can begin. That separation, a difficult task even when 10–20 selective splits have been made in the original protein, is extremely complicated or impossible when 50–100 peptides occur in the mixture. However, some split products obtained with trypsin may be as long as 40 residues, too big for direct sequential analysis by the methods previously discussed. Subsequent treatment with one of the other enzymes is then necessary.

When the amino acid sequences of all peptides obtained from a protein by tryptic splitting have been established, usually by a combination of the previously mentioned methods, there remains the question of the original sequential order of these peptides. This requires the isolation of bridge peptides, which must be obtained by other enzymes or by partial acid hydrolysis (see Fig. 8). These are overlap-

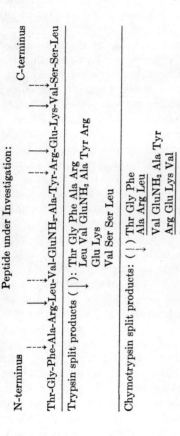

Peptide under Investigation:

N-terminus

C-terminus

Thr-Gly-Phe-Ala-Arg-Leu-Val-GluNH₂-Ala-Tyr-Arg-Glu-Lys-Val-Ser-Ser-Leu

Trypsin split products (↓): Thr Gly Phe Ala Arg
                               Leu Val GluNH₂ Ala Tyr Arg
                               Glu Lys
                               Val Ser Ser Leu

Chymotrypsin split products: (↓) Thr Gly Phe
                                    Ala Arg Leu
                                    Val GluNH₂ Ala Tyr
                                    Arg Glu Lys Val
                                    Ser Ser Leu

Fɪɢ. 8. *Elucidation of amino acid sequence of a heptadecapeptide (17 resi-dues). Trypsin splits 3 peptide bonds next to basic amino acid residues (↓). The original sequential order of the resulting 4 peptides is uniquely fixed by isolating the 2 basic peptides (underlined) of the 5 peptides given by chymo-trypsin, which preferentially splits next to aromatic and hydrophobic residues (↓).*

ping peptides containing sequences from two different tryptic peptides. The fact that all bridge peptides carry at least one basic amino acid residue facilitates their detection and separation from the bulk of the other peptides, which are neutral or, if they contain aspartic or glutamic acid, acidic (the terminal amino and carboxyl groups of each peptide balance one another).

Now that we have made the casual acquaintance of general protein chemistry: What do we know specifically about virus proteins? As stated, most simple viruses appear to be built up of relatively small uniform protein molecules which are attached to one another only by secondary forces, such as hydrogen and hydrophobic bonds and salt linkages. This ability of the small virus protein molecules, that they can form a particle of definite shape and dimensions by progressive aggregation, is as specific and almost as sophisticated a function as are the biological activities of other proteins previously discussed. This ability is lost when the protein is denatured, for it requires the subunits to retain their intrinsic shape with complementary binding sites in the right places to fit and lock one subunit to the other. We are faced here with a three-dimensional structure at different levels of organization. Internal bonds give the subunit a native configuration and shape; external bonds hold one such unit in juxtaposition to the other and cooperatively give the virus its final shape. Therefore, it must be a tricky business to degrade a virus in such a manner as to disrupt the external bonds and set the subunits free without affecting their internal bonds, even though these are of similar nature. Conditions to achieve this have been most carefully worked out for TMV, the chemically best-known virus, and most of the subsequent discussion will be concerned with TMV specifically.

As previously stated this rod-shaped virus is built up of about 2200 roughly ellipsoid or football shaped protein molecules (see Fig. 4). These are obtained in native form if the virus is degraded by weak alkali or by strong (67%) acetic acid, and they retain their shape and their ability to re-form virus rods when so isolated. But strong denaturants with high affinities for protein surfaces, such as the detergents, give the virus protein properties similar to those of the hard boiled egg previously discussed. Such a denatured protein preparation is unsuitable for many purposes, though not necessarily for those requiring further degradation prior to amino acid analysis and sequential studies.

Amino acid analyses of the TMV protein obtained by the automatic amino acid analyzer, not differing very greatly from those obtained during the B.A. (Before Automatization) era, are given in Table I. These are calculated in terms of numbers of amino acid residues per protein molecule. Actually, the determination of the molecular weight of the protein unit was very difficult, because of the previously mentioned tendency of the protein units to stick together or to aggregate, first to a hexamer (6 units combined), then to rings composed of 49 molecules (these, from their appearance on electron micrographs, have been called "doughnuts"), and finally to rods. Early indications that the molecular weight was about 18,000, a value which was only recently established by physico-chemical techniques, came from the amino acid analyses themselves, since they showed the presence of one cysteine and 2 lysine residues per 18,000 molecular weight unit. Definitely, therefore, the true molecular weight could only be 18,000 or a multiple of that value. Other indications came from end group studies to be discussed below.

To return now to the analytical results, it is quite heartening to note that the same amino acid composition was reported by two different laboratories, one in Berkeley, California, and the other in Tübingen, Germany. One research group arrived at the composition by direct analysis of the hydrolyzed protein, while the other summated the analyses of the trypsin split-product peptides, with both groups using the automatic analyser. This amino acid composition is not particularly unusual, compared to that of non-viral proteins (see Table I), except for the fact that

TABLE I

AMINO ACID COMPOSITION OF PROTEINS (RESIDUES PER MOLE)

Amino acid	Tobacco mosaic virus protein[a]					Ribonuclease (cow pancreas)	Lysozyme[b] (chicken eggwhite)
	Common	YA[b]	171	Dahlemense	HR[b]		
Glycine	6	6	6	6	**4**	3	12
Alanine	14	14	**15**	**11**	**18**	12	11
Valine	14	14	14	**15**	**10**	9	6
Leucine	12	12	**13**	**13**	**11**	2	8
Isoleucine	9	**8**	9	**7**[b]	**8**	3	6
Phenylalanine	8	8	8	8	**6**	3	3
Tyrosine	4	4	4	**5**	**7**	6	3
Tryptophan	3	3	3	3	3	0	8
Histidine	0	0	0	0	**1**	4	1
Arginine	11	11	11	**9**	11	4	11
Lysine	2	2	2	2	2	10	6
Aspartic acid	18	**19**	**17**	**17**	**17**	15	20
Glutamic acid	16	16	16	**19**	**22**	12	5
Serine	16	**14**	**17**	16	**13**	15	9
Threonine	16	**17**	**15**	**17**	**14**	10	7
Cysteine	1	1	1	1	1	0	0
Cystine	0	0	0	0	0	4 (×2)	5 (×2)
Methionine	0	0	0	**1**	**0**	4	2
Proline	8	8	**7**	8	**3**	4	2
(—CO)—NH₂	(~20)				8	(~17)	(~18)
Amino acid residues	158	158	158	158	158	124	130

[a] The composition of common TMV and 4 of its strains are given. The data which differ for the strains as compared to common TMV are in boldface. In YA, one isoleucine seems to be replaced by an arginine; in the chemically produced strain 171, one proline, aspartic acid, and threonine are replaced by one leucine, alanine, and serine. The Dahlemense strain shows about 8 replacements; HR, about 18.
[b] These data are less firmly established than the rest.

two amino acids which often play important functional roles in enzymes, namely, histidine and methionine, are completely absent in TMV. One is thus tempted to wonder whether there is a critical significance in this omission. However, amino acid analyses of certain strains of TMV have proven this not to be the case. Most strains or variants of the virus are chemically quite similar to the common strain, although minor differences have been detected in most. However, in a few strains showing more marked chemical variations, either or both histidine and methionine were found to be present (see Table I). Thus, it appears that the significance of the absence of these amino acids from TMV and most of its strains cannot be very decisive.

The important deduction derived from the analytical studies, namely, that the proteins of related strains of a virus are similar but not necessarily identical in composition, will concern us more later. The same situation exists for corresponding proteins of more complex organisms. Thus, the hormone insulin, as isolated from the pancreas of beef or sheep, differs by one amino acid residue. It seems that in a biologically active protein developed for a specific purpose some variations in chemical structure are permitted without loss of function. This could better be stated in more correct evolutionary terms: some of the random variations caused by mutation are not harmful to the function of a given protein; thus they do not endanger the survival of a particular strain or species, and become perpetuated.

Simultaneously with the definite establishment of the amino acid composition of TMV, work on the structural analysis of the virus protein was initiated with a search for its end groups. When Harris and Knight found that the enzyme carboxypeptidase split off about 2200 molecules of threonine from each TMV particle without the release of any other amino acids, it seemed logical to conclude that each of the 2200 protein subunits had a C-terminal threonine and that some structural feature near that threonine prevented further action of the enzyme. This was proven to be the case by chemical methods which confirmed the C-terminal position of the threonine and showed that —prolyl—alanyl— preceded that C-terminal threonine. Proline has the reputation of being a notorious spoil-sport for most proteolytic enzymes, which generally need a regular peptide linkage

$$-CO-NH- \quad \text{rather than} \quad -CO-\overset{\displaystyle R}{\underset{\displaystyle |}{N}}-$$

for their attachment next to the one they intend to split. Thus, it now became understandable why threonine alone was released by carboxypeptidase from the —prolyl—alanyl—threonine sequence of TMV (see p. 96 and Fig. 22 for further discussion of this topic). Soon thereafter, a C-terminal hexapeptide containing 3 additional amino acids was isolated. All 13 strains investigated seemed to share the same terminal tripeptide sequence (—pro—ala—thr), but the so-called HR strain which also differed markedly in amino acid composition (see Table I) was found to differ from TMV and the other strains studied in regard to the next 3 residues.

Now to the amino end: surprisingly, and to the author's considerable disappointment (for he had spent the preceding year abroad acquainting himself with the just then developing N-terminal methodology), no N-terminal groups could be detected in TMV by any means. The situation was confused because similar studies in Germany were interpreted as demonstrating the existence of an N-terminal prolin. Later these authors conceded that this N-terminal prolin was caused by rupture of the protein chain due to their method of isolating the protein. Further claims that this prolin actually closed a loop in the chain were later retracted. The important break-through was the discovery by Narita, a young Japanese scientist visiting our laboratory, that the N-terminal amino acid of TMV was acetylated, a structural feature not previously known to occur in proteins. Thus the chain starts with an acetyl—seryl—tyrosyl group

$$CH_2OH$$
$$|$$
$$CH_3CO—NH—CH—CO—$$

and since the nitrogen loses its basic property upon combination with the acetyl group, it would not be expected to behave as an N-terminal residue in any of the tests previously applied. The same acetyl end was found to exist in all strains of TMV studied. All other plant viruses that have since been studied also lacked N-terminal groups, and in several the acetyl group was again found to be present; but the first and neighboring amino acids were different in each case from the sequence observed in the TMV family and from one to the other. Thus it would appear that an acetylated chain end might represent a characteristic feature of plant viral proteins, a statement that will remain true only until someone finds a virus protein with a free N-terminal residue. It is already known that acetylation is not confined to the viruses, for several mammalian proteins were recently found to terminate in N-acetyl amino acid residues.

The report of the structural analysis of TMV might be interrupted here with a few speculative considerations. The common or type strain of TMV appears to be remarkably stable. While mutants appear frequently, the common strain always seems to be dominant and to outlast and outgrow any mutant in doubly infected plants. Virus that was sent by Stanley to Germany 25 years ago and that has replicated through the era of Hitler's laws for the protection of the super-race and the cataclysm of World War II, is identical in all known respects—and thus, presumably, the same strain—to the one Stanley took with him when he left the Rockefeller Institute at Princeton to found the Virus Laboratory of the University of California. What makes this virus so stable? Possibly just the features we have mentioned above: enzymes which attack proteins from the amino end cannot degrade the virus protein, for it lacks a free amino end. Enzymes which attack proteins from the carboxyl end can take off only one amino acid residue from each chain and do so without damaging or weakening the virus structure or infectivity. Enzymes which attack from the middle, such as trypsin, also do not attack the virus rods, even though they degrade the isolated protein, apparently because the firm packing of protein units in the rod (Fig. 4) forbids access of these enzymes to the susceptible parts of the chain. Finally, the absence of two important amino acids makes the virus an inadequate diet for most microorganisms and thus protects it against those ubiquitous microbes which usually adapt themselves to surmount any nutritional obstacles in their path. In contrast to the marked resistance of TMV and related strains to bacterial spoilage, the previously mentioned HR strain, the "odd ball" mutant which possesses the two amino acids in question (histidine and methionine), spoils as easily as other typical proteins.

If we now return to the main topic, the amino acid sequence of the TMV protein, intensive work has been done since 1954 at the University of California Virus Laboratory by Niu, Gish, Ramachandran, Narita, Tsugita, Young, and, last and least, by the author, along the general lines indicated above. Trypsin failed to split one of the 11 arginine bonds and one of the two lysine bonds, thus yielding a total of 12 peptides which were separated and analyzed for composition and for sequence. One peptide termed the I-peptide, because it tends to be insoluble, presented particular problems. It is longer than any previously analyzed peptide (41 residues); it lacks an N-terminal group, since it is from the original N-acetyl end of the molecule; it obviously lacks internal basic groups susceptible to attack by trypsin; and it is very rich in hydrophobic and amide groups (leucine, glutamine, etc.). This peptide has a tendency to aggregate to high molecular weight material and may thus represent the part of the protein which is particularly responsible for its tendency to aggregate to rods. The high leucine content appears significant in this connection, since in another case of protein aggregation (insulin fibril formation) this has been found to be largely due to the interaction of hydrophobic groups.

Since about 1958, two laboratories in Tübingen have been engaged in careful work along similar lines, aided by the development of a new technique of separating the tryptic peptides obtained from TMV. The results obtained by Anderer and his co-workers and by Wittman are in general accord with the findings of our laboratory. In the summer of 1960, an almost complete structure for the TMV protein was proposed by one of these groups headed by Schramm, a report which represented an important advance, since it meant that they had found all the bridge peptides necessary to interconnect the tryptic peptides in proper sequence. Minor parts of this sequence were not in agreement with the results obtained at Berkeley, particularly in regard to the I-peptide, but enough of it was in accord to show that the conclusions were based on sound experimental work. A few months later, the work at our laboratory had advanced to a point where the missing sequences in the structure proposed by the German group could be filled in and their sequential arrangement of the peptides could be confirmed. Thus, there remain only a few minor differences to be ironed out between the structures proposed by the two laboratories.

TMV protein represents the first protein that has had its complete amino acid sequence elucidated by two research teams (Fig. 9). This appears of particular importance, since, with 158 residues, TMV is also the longest peptide chain analyzed to date. Other proteins on which work has been completed are the hormone insulin (51 residues), and the enzyme ribonuclease (124 residues). The difficulties inherent in this type of work are such that the added confidence engendered by the close agreement in the results of two research groups is of great value in establishing the validity and reliability of such analyses. But it must not be forgotten that the real structure of a protein, such as that of TMV, is a three-dimensional one, and that we have as

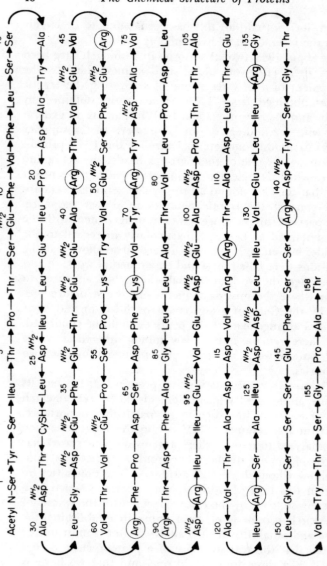

FIG. 9. Sequence of the 158 amino acid residues in the protein subunit of the common strain of tobacco mosaic virus. The basic amino acid residues which represent sites of attack by trypsin are circled. They subdivide the protein into 12 peptides, all but one of which terminate in arginine (10) or lysine (1). The first (residue 1–41) represents the I peptide, with its acetylated end group.

yet only inadequate, and very laborious methods to determine the three-dimensional folding of the chain. Interestingly enough, recent work suggests that the folding of proteins may take place automatically and be dictated by the amino acid sequence alone.

To some, the problems of amino acid sequence may seem picayunish. "Who cares whether the 108th residue from the amino end is leucine or valine?" they may say. Such questions and doubts may appear at first sight not unreasonable. Obviously, any research man is thrilled by new facts, in the same manner as an explorer gets excited when he sees a new mountain or a lake not previously charted. Yet, when confronted with the practical man's question: so what?, he may not be ready with a convincing answer. For he is embarrassed to confess the main basis of his exhilaration: I did not know, I wondered, and now I know. But at a later time, the newly discovered mountain or lake may fit into a bigger pattern showing the course of a geological fault and contributing to our understanding of the shaping of the earth's crust. In the same way, beyond any doubt, specific knowledge of the protein structure of a virus will—no, already does—contribute to our understanding of the mechanisms of inheritance and, thus, of life itself. Some earlier speculations concerning the survival value to the virus of the acetyl group on one end and of the proline near the other have illustrated this fact. Other experimental data will be discussed later which show that the elucidation of the complete sequence of this protein may be an important stepping stone towards a very general and profound intellectual goal.

Very much less is known about the protein structure of all other viruses. Quite a number of viruses have been analyzed for their amino acid composition, but frequently by methods now obsolete. End-group studies have indicated the absence of N-terminal groups in all the plant virus proteins that have been studied. C-terminal analyses, both enzymatic and chemical, have suggested the presence of many subunits, and the belief that all viruses are built up from aggregates of separate peptide chains has been supported by the observations that they are generally dis-aggregated into low molecular weight proteins by detergents and other H-bond breaking agents. However, the subunits of many viruses may be 2–4 times bigger than those of TMV.

The chemistry of the nucleic acids

AS PREVIOUSLY MENTIONED, the nucleic acid represents the business end of the virus. It alone can do everything the virus can do, even though inefficiently. Thus, the chemical structure of the nucleic acids must be regarded as the key problem of virology and one of the most crucial problems of biology as a whole. If we add to this the statement that nucleic acid chemistry is on several counts not nearly as complex as protein chemistry, then the curiosity of the reader may become sufficiently aroused for him to start thumbing to the end of the chapter to peek at the final solution, the complete structure of the viral gene. He may save himself the trouble. Unfortunately, certain aspects of the structure of nucleic acids represent, as we will see, serious obstacles to rapid progress in this field, and, thus, this chapter will contain more unanswered questions and fewer solid achievements than the preceding chapter on the proteins.

The principles of nucleic acid structure are similar to those of protein structure. Again we are dealing with long-chain polymers. The monomer unit of ribonucleic acid (RNA) is called a nucleotide and is the result of the condensation of three components: a ring compound containing nitrogen and carbon, called the base, condensed in a so-called glycosidic linkage with a 5-carbon sugar, ribose, which in turn is esterified with phosphoric acid (Fig. 10).

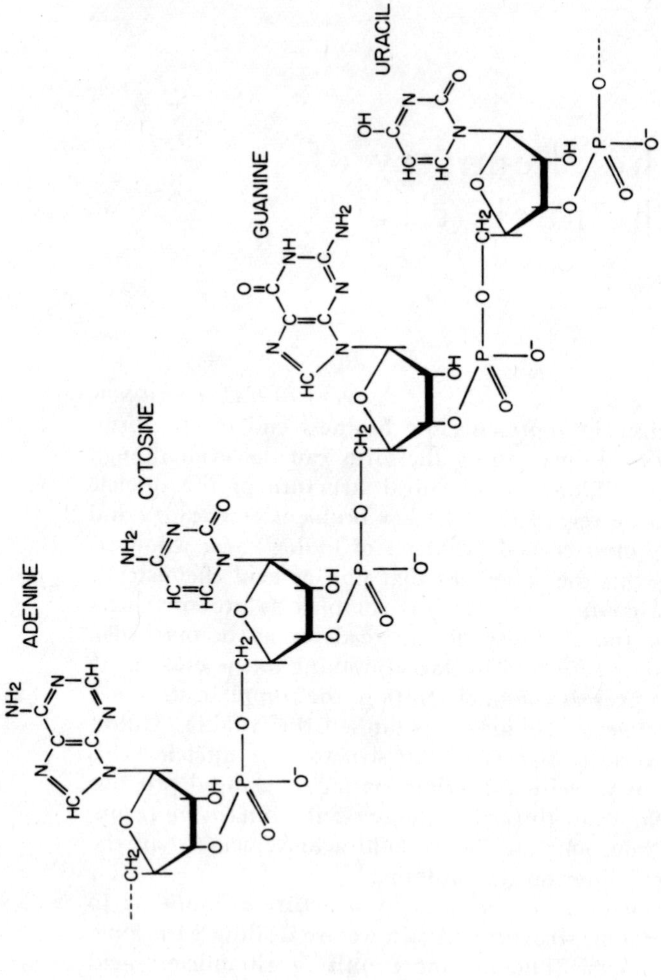

Fig. 10. A. Chemical structure of ribonucleotides. The four nucleotides are shown in chain linkage.

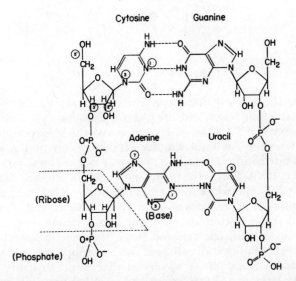

Fig. 10. *B. The two complementary pairs of bases (cytosine-guanine, adenine-uracil) are shown in the hydrogen bonded (————) state which they tend to form when possible. The three building blocks of each nucleotide (phosphate, ribose, base) are delineated.*

Both the ribose and the phosphoric acid have extra hydroxyl groups and can easily undergo double esterification, thus forming the chain molecule, —phosphate—ribose—phosphate—ribose—. This corresponds to the backbone of the peptide chain of proteins (III) while the bases of the

$$\begin{array}{c} \rangle\text{—N—C—C—}\rangle\text{—N—C—C—}\rangle\text{—N—C—C—}\langle \\ \text{H} \quad \text{H} \quad \text{O} \quad \text{H} \quad \text{H} \quad \text{O} \quad \text{H} \quad \text{H} \quad \text{O} \end{array}$$

III

RNA which are called adenine, guanine, cytosine and uracil, and which are often represented simply by their initials, A, G, C, and U, correspond to the R-groups of the proteins which give the chain molecule its specific character. The structure of an RNA segment is shown in detail in Fig. 10, and in the form of the now customary diagrammatic representation as follows:

Here the vertical lines represent the ribose; the letters on top, the four bases; and the p's, the phosphate ester bridges between the 3' carbon of one sugar and the 5' carbon of the next sugar. An even simpler representation of the same octa-nucleotide is as follows: p A p G p U p C p C p G p A p U. RNA naturally occurs not only in viruses, but in every cell, and while some types of cellular RNA have small amounts of other bases in addition to A, G, C, and U, virus RNA seems to contain only these four common ones.

Deoxyribonucleic acid, or DNA, the genetic material of all real organisms as well as of the bacteriophages and some animal viruses, shows a very similar basic structure. Its sugar lacks one —OH group and is called deoxyribose; instead of uracil, DNA contains 5-methyluracil, or thymine; the rest is the same. In DNA there also occur small amounts of several additional bases and, very peculiarly, the DNA of a particular group of bacteriophages contains 5-(hydroxymethyl)cytosine in place of cytosine with varying amounts of glucose attached to that base.

If we now look again at the structure of the polymer, be it RNA or DNA, you will notice that each phosphate group carries a negative charge. Phosphoric acid is a triple threat of an acid (it can release 3 hydrogen ions)

and esterification of two of its potentially dissociating groups by ribose, or any other alcohol (R—OH)

$$O=P{\overset{OH}{\underset{O^-}{\diagup}}}OH \xrightarrow{+ROH} O=P{\overset{O-R}{\underset{O^-}{\diagup}}}OH \xrightarrow{+ROH} O=P{\overset{O-R}{\underset{O^-}{\diagup}}}O-R$$
$$+ H_2O \qquad\qquad + H_2O$$

makes the third one the strongest acid. Thus, nucleic acids are acids as strong as sulfuric acid; they burn and char any biological material they come in contact with, including themselves, thereby committing suicide and ending up as bases, caramelized sugar, and free phosphoric acid. What is the catch? How can an ubiquitous cellular component be at the same time such a murderous weapon? The answer is very simple: nucleic acids as such do not exist, their name being in error, for we are always dealing with salts of nucleic acid, nucleates, which means that a positive metal ion is bound to each phosphate, rather than an H^+ ion. Most "nucleic acid" preparations are sodium nucleates, although divalent metal ions such as calcium or magnesium are bound with greater affinity and readily displace the sodium. And obviously, the sodium or calcium nucleates, like the salts of sulfuric, phosphoric, or any other strong acid, are neutral and generally harmless to biological systems.

If we now want to learn more about the chemical nature of biologically active nucleic acids (or rather, nucleates), we naturally focus our attention on the only variable part of the molecule, the four bases. And the first question is: How much is there of each, and is the composition characteristically different for each type of nucleic acid? As previously discussed, the composition of most proteins, in terms of amino acid residues, varies quite markedly, although family resemblances can be detected in related proteins. In nucleic acids there is obviously much less potential variation, there being only four components. And actually, the observed range of variation is not very great in nucleic acids, although differences can usually be detected. A few examples are listed in Table II, to indicate the range of variation. Two important facts are also illustrated in this table. First, in DNA two of the bases generally occur with the same frequency, in pairs: thus, the adenine content

TABLE II

BASE COMPOSITION OF VARIOUS NUCLEIC ACID PREPARATIONS (MOLE %)

Origin of nucleic acid	Guanine	Adenine	Cytosine	Thymine	Uracil	$\dfrac{A + T \text{ (or U)}}{G + C}$
DNA from						
Pseudomonas tabaci (bacterium)	33.7	16.2	33.7	16.4		0.48
Escherichia coli W (bacterium)	25.7	25.1	25.9	23.4		0.94
Clostridium perfringens (bacterium)	15.8	34.1	15.1	35.0		2.24
T2 bacteriophage	18.2	32.5	16.8[a]	32.5		1.86
T5 bacteriophage	19.5	30.3	19.5	30.8		1.57
φX174 (small bacteriophage)	24.1	24.6	18.5	32.8		(1.39)
RNA from						
Tobacco mosaic virus (*all strains*)	25.8	29.3	18.1		26.8	(1.27)
Turnip yellows mosaic virus	17.2	22.6	38.1		22.1	(0.81)
Potato X virus	21.8	34.2	22.8		21.3	(1.24)
Poliomyelitis virus	25.4	30.4	19.5		24.7	(1.23)
Influenza virus (*all strains*)	20.0	23.0	24.5		32.5	(1.24)

[a] Hydroxymethylcytosine.

almost always equals the thymine content; and the cytosine, the guanine content. This phenomenon is observed with surprising regularity, if one attributes small deviations to limitations in the accuracy of analysis. Its great significance in regard to DNA structure will be discussed later. The second important fact illustrated in Table II is that in regard to RNA composition, the various strains of any one virus, such as those of TMV, do not vary noticeably from one another, in contrast to the RNA compositions of different viruses, which are clearly different. The family resemblance to the point of seeming identity in the RNA of strains is a disturbing observation which certainly suggests that composition is not the only means for the differentiation of RNA. For it must be remembered that virus strains generally differ from one another in the disease symptoms they evoke and often in their protein composition; and since the RNA alone can transmit all these viral properties from generation to generation, it, too, must differ from one strain to another. One must therefore conclude that the differences in the makeup of the RNA of close relatives are too subtle to be detected by our present methods for base composition analysis.

A few words about the methods of analysis may be interjected here. As in all polymers, degradation to the level of monomeric building blocks is usually the first step of analysis. The phosphate ester bond to the 5′ —OH group of the ribose of RNA is quite labile to alkali (normal, i.e., 5.6%, potassium hydroxide), and the molecule thus falls apart into nucleotides in this solvent in 18 hours at 37° C. Hot strong acid, on the other hand, breaks down both RNA and DNA to the bases, sugar decomposition products, and phosphoric acid. Finally, the action of two enzymes contained in snake venoms breaks down the nucleic acids into nucleosides (i.e., base + sugar) and phosphate.

The nucleotides, nucleosides, or bases, whichever the case might be, are then separated by one of several methods similar to those employed for the separation of amino acids. One method makes use of paper chromatography, a most generally useful tool introduced into biochemistry about 20 years ago by Martin and Synge. To describe its operation very simply, a spot of a mixture of substances is applied to a sheet of filter paper, the edge of which is then dipped into a solvent mixture, usually containing an alcohol or a less hydrophilic organic compound saturated with water. The solvent slowly travels through the paper by capillarity, and the compounds in the mixture also move, but at different rates, depending on whether they are more hydrophilic and stay in the water preferentially adsorbed by the paper, or whether they are more hydrophobic and move with the organic solvent. Different compounds can thus be separated. Figure 11 illustrates one of several possible experimental setups in which the solvent and sample travel upwards and which is therefore called ascending chromatography. The four bases in RNA and DNA are chemically sufficiently different to separate neatly into four zones under such conditions.

Other techniques take advantage of differences in the ionic charges of different molecules. Each of the bases, like the amino acids, exhibits acidic and basic characteristics, though they are weak in both respects and behave as acids or bases only at quite high or low pH, respectively. Such separations according to charge are produced by applying an electric potential, and the technique is called electrophoresis. It can be performed in a variety of ways, including, quite conveniently, a technique with heavy filter paper. In this case, both ends of the paper are dipped into electrode vessels and wetted with a salt solution to act as conductor, so that when the potential is applied, the charged molecules or ions move (see Fig. 12). The same principle applies when columns (i.e., glass tubes filled with so-called ion exchange resins) are used. Such insoluble resins (usually synthetic polymers) have many strong acidic or basic groups on their surface. When the mixture of purine and pyrimidine bases is added to the top of a tube containing an acidic resin and a salt solution is slowly passed through the tube, the bases will be bound and thus retarded depending

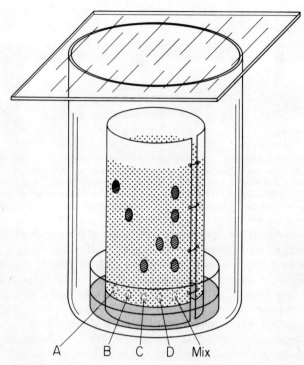

Fig. 11. *Schematic presentation of an ascending paper chromatogram. The four components of the mix are tentatively identified as A, B, C, and D, since they migrate up the paper cylinder as far as the four known markers. The materials are presumed to be colored and directly visible, but this is not a necessary requirement for the use of chromatography.*

on their basicity, the most basic coming off the column last. All these methods are naturally more complicated than it might seem from such brief descriptions, but they are of great adaptability and of immense usefulness for the separation of all kinds of mixtures, such as bases, nucleotides, amino acids, peptides, and proteins.

A very important practical aspect of all such fractionation methods has until now been avoided: How do we find

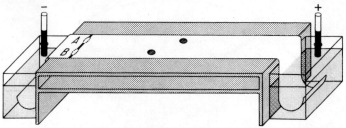

FIG. 12. *Schematic oversimplified presentation of a setup for paper electrophoresis. Actually, the paper strip must at all times be kept equally moist with a salt solution and uniformly cooled to counteract the heat developed through the electric current. The paper is usually covered and hermetically sealed with a glass plate, and water sprays against the bottom of the supporting plate to keep it cooled.*

the material we are interested in on a big sheet of filter paper, or in hundreds of test tubes, each containing a few drops of salt solution collected as it drips out of the resin tube? The term chromatography means color writing, and the first successful applications of this principle were with colored substances, such as the green chlorophylls, or the orange-red carotenoids of plants. But amino acids and nucleotides are colorless substances. Well, with the amino acids it is necessary to form colored derivatives. The reagent introduced in 1945 by Sanger for the detection of N-terminal amino acids, and applicable to all amino acids in an hydrolyzate, fluorodinitrobenzene, makes them bright yellow and easily visible on paper or in solution (see p. 35). Another reagent (ninhydrin) combines with amino acids to give a purple dye, and this is the one used in the automatic amino acid analyzer previously mentioned (p. 35). The ninhydrin reaction also works well on paper. Actually, all kinds of color reactions can be performed on paper. Thus, by a series of test solutions sprayed onto a paper chromatogram containing a number of amino acids or peptides, one can locate (1) those having free amino groups, (2) those having peptide bonds, (3) those containing tryptophan, (4) those containing tyrosine, (5) those containing histidine, (6) those containing arginine, (7) those containing proline, (8) those containing sulfur (cysteine, cystine, and methionine), and (9) probably others that at the moment escape me. Since I indicated in Figs. 11 and 12 the location of different materials by dark spots, it must be assumed that the substances were naturally colored or that the paper cylinder or sheet had been treated with a reagent that revealed them.

But here I got carried away into peptide chemistry when we were supposed to be discussing, primarily, the detection of nucleotides or purine and pyrimidine bases. Was this an attempt at escape from a difficult or unpleasant subject? Far from it, for the detection of these bases is easier than that of the amino acids and not much more difficult than that of colored compounds. We have previously referred to the fact that certain amino acids absorb ultraviolet light. Tryptophan is the prime example, with tyrosine and phenylalanine being much less active in this regard. What these have in common is a so-called conjugated double bond system, meaning carbon atoms being alternatingly singly and doubly bonded, such as

$$H-C=C-C=C-C=C-H$$

Six such carbons in a ring, i.e., the benzene ring

as it occurs in phenylalanine, absorb a little ultraviolet (or, to-the-human-eye-invisible) light, mainly of a wave length of about 260 mμ. Tyrosine, containing one —OH group in addition to the benzene ring, absorbs almost 10 times as strongly with a maximum at 275 mμ; tryptophan, with one more conjugated double bond and an >NH group, absorbs again 4 times stronger, maximally at 280 mμ (see Fig. 13). If the above conjugated chain of 6 is extended to 11 double bonds (40 carbon atoms), the absorption shifts all the way into the visible part of the spectrum,

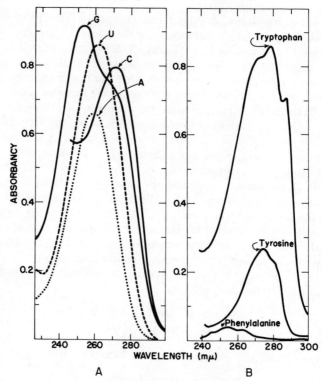

FIG. 13. *A Ultraviolet absorption spectra of nucleosides. A (adenosine) was plotted at 0.01 mg/ml; the others, at 0.02 mg/ml. A and U (uridine) show maximal absorbance near 260 mμ; C (cytosine), about 270 mμ; G (guanine), a less regular shaped absorption curve with a maximum about 250 mμ. B. ultra violet absorption spectra of amino acids which absorb UV light. The amino acids are plotted at similar concentration (0.035 mg/ml). At higher concentration, phenylalanine shows a more characteristic three-peak pattern. The absorption of tyrosine is greatly increased and shifted toward the right in alkaline solution.*

and we observe the bright orange color of the carotenoids previously mentioned (absorption maximum about 490 mμ; visible color is of wave lengths 400–700 mμ). Thus there exists a continuity of spectra, related to chemical structure, and our differentiation between colored substances and those absorbing UV light has no firm physicochemical basis but is dictated by the physiological limitations of the human eye, which fails below 350–400 mμ.

Again the object of this discussion, the detection of the purines and pyrimidines, seems to have eluded us, but now we are actually getting close. These bases also have conjugated double bonds, as well as nitrogen, and 3 of them also have oxygen atoms. Thus they absorb strongly (2–3 times stronger than tryptophan) with maxima ranging from 250 mμ for guanine to 280 μ for cytosine (see Fig. 13). Thus UV absorption is a very convenient tool first for their detection, and secondly for their quantitative determination. Detection is possible by means of photography, since the photographic plate is sensitive to lower wave lengths than the human eye. However, the eye can actually do the trick too. For if a sheet of paper is illuminated with a strong UV light source in a dark room, it fluoresces, i.e., it appears whitish to the eye. However, materials in the paper which absorb the UV light prevent or quench that fluorescence, and dark spots are seen where such materials are concentrated. Thus, chromatograms of nucleotides or bases, which look uniformly white in daylight, show distinct dark spots when inspected in the dark under a strong UV light source. These spots are circled with a pencil, cut out, extracted with a known amount of a suitable solvent, and then analyzed in a spectrophotometer. The shape of the absorption curve and particularly the wave length of maximal absorption verifies the identification of the substance in question, and the height of that maximum tells the investigator the concentration of the substance in solution (Fig. 13). This concentration, multiplied by the volume of solution, tells him how much material he has, a figure which is usually expressed in micrograms, or millionth of grams (1 ounce = 28 g), for the methods are so sensitive that it is best to work with amounts of less than 1 mg of RNA.

In principle, there is no difference between colorimetric methods, which have long been used to measure colored materials with reference to a known standard color, and spectrophotometric methods, which permit the direct measurement of the absorption at a selected wave length. The fact that spectrophotometry could be extended to wave lengths beyond the range of human vision, however, has proven of immense usefulness in facilitating the study of intricate biological processes. For now the presence and the amount of proteins and nucleic acids, these two pillars of molecular biology, as well as of many products derived from these, can be monitored quickly, easily, and without loss of material in any well equipped laboratory.

The results of the analyses for the four (or more) bases in a sample of nucleic acid are usually expressed in relative terms, such as the mole percentage of each of the four bases: out of 100 bases, so many and so many are guanine, adenine, cytosine, and uracil, respectively (see Table II). Other ways of expressing the data are also used, e.g., percent on a weight basis, but never the nice clear method of expression which is now preferred for proteins: each molecule of TMV protein has 1 cysteine, 2 lysine, etc. residues. For this there exist several good, though unfortunate, reasons: this expression requires an exact knowledge of the molecular weight of the macromolecule; it also requires that the sample under study be homogeneous, which means that all molecules in the sample are identical; it finally requires, or at least prefers, that the macromolecule not be enormously big, so that the components occur in reasonably low numbers, such as 1 to 18 for the amino acids in TMV. With nucleic acids these requirements are rarely fulfilled. Most nucleic acid preparations, but particularly those from organs or organisms such as yeast RNA or thymus DNA (which are frequently analyzed and used as reference substances), are quite heterogeneous mixtures of many different molecular species and of different molecular weights. Probably the only big molecular nucleic acids which are naturally uniform are those of viruses, and particularly the RNA from small highly purified viruses such as TMV, or poliomyelitis. In the case of TMV we are reasonably certain that the virus particles are uniform in length and thus in weight, except for the fact that a certain percentage (10–20%) of the rods in most preparations are usually broken, and that another 10–20% of the RNA chains seem to tear in the course of isolation. The molecular weight of an intact chain of TMV-RNA, as calculated from the RNA content and the particle weight of the virus, is 5.2% of 40 million, or 2.1 million. This is in good agreement with molecular weight determinations by physicochemical methods (light scattering or analytical ultracentrifugation coupled with measurements of viscosity or diffusion). And from this value, and the proportion of the four bases found, the total number of nucleotides, and the number of each per molecule can and has been calculated. These figures are 1680 guanylic, 1900 adenylic, 1180 cytidylic, and 1740 uridylic acids.

But let us not forget that analytical results never have absolute meaning but are only more or less close approximations to the truth. Thus, if we assume that the analyses of the bases in TMV-RNA has a 1% error, meaning that it is within 1% of the truth, we would (after having congratulated the analyst for being so unusually exact) have to modify the above composition by saying that there are 1680 ± 8 guanylic, 1900 ± 10 adenylic, 1180 ± 6 cytidylic, and 1740 ± 9 uridylic acid residues per molecule of TMV-RNA. In other words, referring back to the point made above, the high molecular weight of the nucleic acid makes the expression of analytical results in the form of residues per mole rather meaningless. Furthermore, we now see that the lack of detectable differences in the composition of the nucleic acids of different virus strains, which we have previously mentioned, does not signify identity in composition. For even with good analytical precision, an exchange of 10 or more nucleotides would remain below the level of detectability. This is the bane of dealing with awfully big molecules, molecules such as TMV-RNA, which is 100 times as big as the TMV-protein, which is in turn 100 times as big as the glucose molecule, which is in turn 180 times as big as a hydrogen atom.

While we are discussing the relative size of things, it is good to recall that viral RNA, one of the biggest definite molecules known to occur in nature, is just barely within the range of the electron microscope. One ounce of RNA, probably more than the total viral RNA prepared all over the world since its discovery, contains about 10^{19} molecules, a figure with 19 zeros after the 1, or a million times a million times ten million.

Yet one must also remember that TMV-RNA is as small as any genetically active nucleic acid and that most DNA molecules are probably 50 to 5000 times bigger. Besides, the total amount of chromosomal DNA in a human cell is about a million times that of the nucleic acid of a TMV particle. But this is what one might expect considering that the one carries enough genetic information to specify a man and the other a virus.

A class of RNA molecules much smaller than those of viruses and cytoplasmic particles has been detected which fulfills important functions in helping the cell machinery to build up proteins, but these are definitely not related to the genetic nucleic acids of viruses or cells. We will come back to the function of this so-called transport RNA later.

Having surveyed some of the techniques of nucleotide analysis and composition, we now return to the subject of nucleic acid structure. As stated, both RNA and DNA seem to represent very long chains of nucleotides, without break or branching. We have earlier seen that the other biologically important class of chain molecules, the proteins, derive many of their specific capabilities from their three-dimensional structure, which is due to the folding of peptide chains into a definite and unique pattern, held in place by a variety of secondary valences. In discussing the existence and the role of secondary structure in nucleic acids, we shall begin with DNA, because a definite three-dimensional model of the structure of DNA was proposed by Watson and Crick in 1953, and many important subsequent findings have given added support to this hypothesis. This model is based on two main experimental lines of evidence: the physicists' study of X-ray scattering diagrams of DNA, which enabled them to detect and measure the order in the spatial arrangement of its atoms; and the chemists' base analyses of DNA, which, as previously mentioned, showed that the content of A usually equaled that of T, while the content of G equaled that of C (Table II). Considering these data, as well as the chemical structure of the four bases, Watson and Crick proposed a double-stranded helical structure for DNA, according to which the two chains, twisted around one another, were held together by crossbonds perpendicular to the long axis of the molecule; crossbonds attributed to the hydrogen-bonded interaction of specific pairs of bases (Figs. 14, 15*). An inspection of the structures of the bases shows that adenine and thymine complement one another in a manner suitable for the establishment of 2 hydrogen bonds, a $—C{=}O$ group facing an $H_2N—$ group and an NH group facing an N. Quite similarly, cytosine fits to guanine, possibly in triply-bonded interaction (Figs. 10, 15).

It has been suggested, and seems easy to imagine, that during the replication process each base of a single-stranded DNA would select and hold in place its complementary base, or rather, nucleotide derivative. These would then only have to establish phosphate ester connections to their neighbors and the result would be a new DNA chain of a specific base sequence, complementary to the original, which in turn, upon similar replication, would reproduce the original chain. Thus the sequence in line (a) will dictate the complementary chain (b), which in turn, by the same mechanism, produces (c), a replicate of (a),

(a) p A p G p T p T p C p A p C p G p G p T p A p C p C p

(b) p T p C p A p A p G p T p G p C p C p A p T p G p G p

(c) p A p G p T p T p C p A p C p G p G p T p A p C p C p

(The small p indicates the phosphate groups holding the chain together. The capital letters are meant to represent

* Figure 15 in section of figures at end of book.

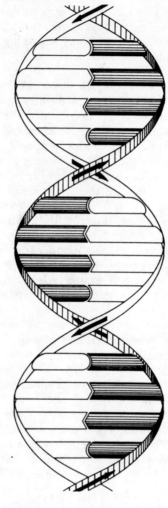

Fig. 14. The Watson-Crick model of DNA structure. A diagrammatic representation showing a white polynucleotide strand (descending) and a black strand (ascending), the two held together by the bases forming rungs of the ladder owing to their paired hydrogen bonding.

the 4 deoxyribonucleotides.) Here, for the first time, the important biological process of reproduction was explained on the chemical level. Ingenious experiments with isotope-labelled DNA, performed a few years ago by Meselson and Stahl, have come very close to proving that this is actually the mechanism of intracellular replication.

While there are still some problems connected with this scheme of molecular reproduction, such as the question of how the chains can separate prior to replication, the mental image of DNA as such a double-stranded twisted rope has become firmly established. Most of the properties of DNA are well accounted for by this structure. We might briefly list a few more of these. We have discussed the UV absorbing property of nucleotides. However, when the bases are in a position to interact with their complementary mates, and possibly also with their neighbors, their absorption is decreased by one-third or more. In intact, that is, double-stranded, DNA, the absorption is so decreased. Other physical properties, such as optical rotation and viscosity, are also changed in the expected direction by the bonded structure.

Before discussing the effect of agents which tend to separate the two strands, we will briefly consider the action of agents, be they chemical or enzymatic, which attack and break phosphodiester bonds along the chain. This has at first no marked effect on the molecule as a whole, just as a ladder tends to retain its shape when its uprights are cut in isolated places; but additional breaks become increasingly dangerous to the structure of DNA, since each has a progressively greater chance to fall opposite, or almost opposite, to a previous break, and soon the structure collapses. When one plots the effect of the number of breaks on the integrity of such a structure as a whole, one obtains what is called a multi-hit type of curve. The initial lag in this curve, as shown in Fig. 16, clearly distinguishes it from the single-hit curve, characteristic for the degradation of a single chain molecule under attack by a chain-breaking agent.

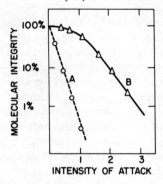

Fɪɢ. 16. *Typical single-hit (A) and multi-hit (B) curves. The attack might be measured in minutes of treatment by an agent such as an enzyme or X-rays. It might also represent the number of cuts in the average molecule. The molecular integrity might be measured physico-chemically (molecular weight, viscosity), or biologically (infectivity, genetic activity).*

The effect of hydrogen-bond-breaking agents on such a molecule is naturally of considerable interest. This effect can be likened to the cutting of the rungs of the ladder. First, one is struck by the great resistance of the structure of DNA to the action of such agents. Thus, heat denatures most proteins readily, with temperatures above 40° being harmful to some (e.g., TMV protein) and 60–70°, to almost all. In contrast, DNA usually must be heated to 90° or more before its structure collapses. Interestingly enough, a DNA particularly rich in G and C, the triply bonded pair of bases, is considerably more heat-resistant than is a DNA rich in A and T. While urea in high concentrations denatures proteins readily, it affects DNA only in conjunction with heat, decreasing the temperature at which the structure of the molecule collapses. Detergents and soaps don't find any hydrophobic sites of attachment and thus do not affect the structure of nucleic acids. The DNA molecule is rather sensitive to acid solutions, because the bonds between the purine bases and the deoxy sugars break easily in acid. But DNA is particularly defenseless against one seemingly harmless agent, and that is distilled, i.e., salt-free, water. For in the absence of other negative ions (the positive counter ions, e.g., Na$^+$, are naturally and necessarily present in a neutral DNA solution) the phosphate groups on the molecule, owing to their strong negative charge and close proximity, strongly repel one another, thereby stretching out the chain and disrupting the helical twist. It is in this manner that the removal of salts effectively denatures DNA in the cold. The term "denaturation" as used here, as well as with proteins, means the disruption of the original, natural or "native" secondary, that is, largely hydrogen bonded, structure. The properties of denatured DNA differ from those of native DNA in the expected manner. Thus, it shows a higher UV absorption and lower optical rotation and viscosity.

One remarkable exception to all we have said has been discovered in recent years. The DNA of a group of very unusually small bacteriophages, of lower molecular weight than respectable DNA samples, also shows in the natural state all the properties of denatured DNA, or, in other words, it seems to be single stranded, lacking any detectable fixed and orderly three-dimensional structure. This is also borne out by the composition of such DNA (see Table II) which fails to show the equality of A and T, or G and C, characteristic of double-stranded DNA.

We now turn back to the RNA of viruses. This chain molecule seems to behave like the last mentioned DNA and unlike the typical double-stranded DNA. In the presence of salts, the bases appear to interact, as shown by the usual criteria (lowered absorption, higher optical rotation, etc.), though probably to an extent limited by the irregular non-complementary base sequences (Fig. 17). Removal of salts reverses the physical phenomena indicative of bonding. But with RNA this cannot be called denaturation, since it proceeds without any loss of biological activity and in readily reversible manner. Thus, one can conclude that the same principal forces govern all nucleic acid molecules. In the case of RNA, base-interaction and, possibly, helical twist are unnecessary luxuries which the molecules accept to the

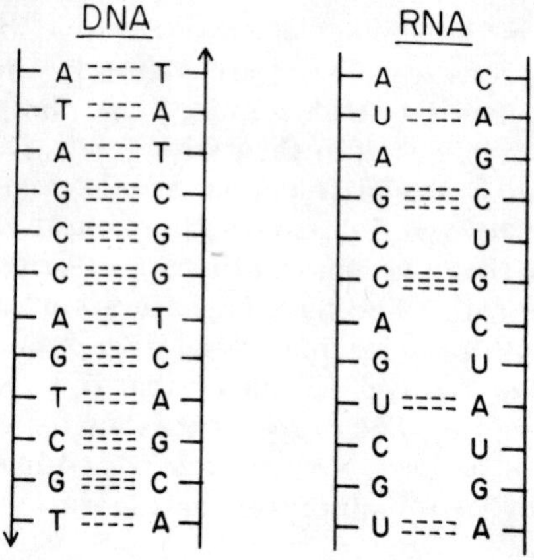

FIG. 17. *Hydrogen bonding between complementary chains (DNA) and random-sequence chains (RNA). The double H-bonds holding adenine (A) to thymine (T) or uracil (U) and the triple bonds between guanine (G) and cytosine (C) are indicated by double or triple dashed lines. The drawing represents untwisted double helices. In the case of DNA, each base finds itself opposite a complementary one on the other chain, maximal bonding is possible, and the structure is most stable. In the case of RNA, bonding is possible only where complementary bases happen to meet by chance; bonding is therefore limited, and the double stranded structure is weak.*

extent offered by the circumstances and give up without harm under changing circumstances. In contrast, typical DNA appears to be born with the golden spoon of stabilizing double-strandedness in its mouth, but "comes the revolution," and this more sophisticated molecule is lost. Actually, there have been recent reports by Marmur and Doty that the verdict is not always and necessarily final. For if homogeneous DNA, denatured at 100°, is allowed to anneal for a long time at temperatures of 60–70°, then some chains or part of chains seem to find it possible to realign themselves with complementary chains and thus re-form stable double-stranded and biologically active molecules. Such a phenomenon is called reversible denaturation and has also been observed with proteins whose secondary and tertiary structure had been extensively disrupted. But it would be more startling a phenomenon in the case of DNA if really complete denaturation and chain separation were followed by the re-formation of many thousands of specific bonds and the reconstruction of the original double helix.

To return to the prime function of nucleic acids: they carry genetic information. And since this function does not require any fixed secondary structure in the case of RNA, nor for at least certain types of DNA, it seems that this kind of activity is not a function of any secondary structure. Thus, typical DNA may benefit from retaining "for life" the double strandedness with which it was born. But this may be only for purposes of stabilization, similar to the functional role of the proteins covering the RNA of viruses. There remains thus nothing but the primary structure of nucleic acids to account for their prime biological role. And this structure, as we mentioned earlier, would be a monotonous sequence of —sugar—phosphate—sugar—phosphate— residues, were it not for the presence and the order of the bases along that chain.

We have now arrived at the main bottleneck in the development of this important field of molecular biology. The problem of establishing the sequential order of four bases in a 6500 unit or longer chain is considerably more difficult than that of determining the sequence of 16 types of amino acids in a 158 member chain. And the situation is even worse, since the development of methods to determine even short nucleotide sequences lags far behind that for peptide analysis. Particularly lacking for nucleic acids is a selective splitting agent corresponding in its action to that of trypsin acting on proteins and yielding relatively long and reproducible fragments. The most selective enzymes now available for RNA break the molecule at an average of about every fourth bond, and we know that all possible di-, tri-, and tetra-nucleotide combinations occur, as one might expect. The relative frequency of their occurrence appears to vary from one RNA to another, including that of some of the strains of TMV which seem to have the same nucleotide composition. This is an important finding, since it supplies the first chemically detectable difference in the RNA of genetically close relatives. However, it would appear that only the establishment of much longer sequences would begin to supply data which would lead to a decipherment of the code relating nucleic acid structure to genetic function, and in particular to protein structure. We will have more to say about this problem later.

With DNA, the problem of nucleotide sequence is more complex, the dearth of methods the same, and the data equally limited. An ingenious recently devised method to determine the frequency of nearest neighbor combinations in DNA has supplied a set of data characteristically different for the DNA of different species, but no further sequences beyond those of dinucleotides can be obtained by this method.

The important techniques that opened the door to recent advances in the elucidation of protein structure were the methods of end-group analysis, and the same approach appears logical in the case of nucleic acids. Here again, the situation is in two respects somewhat more complex. First, each of the two terminal nucleotides may or may not carry an extra phosphate which naturally influences its behavior. And secondly, one end group in a 6500 unit or longer chain represents more of an analytical problem and yields less information than one chain end in a 20–158 unit long peptide chain. Yet, progress along these lines is being made, largely through the use of radioactive labels and purified enzymes. Methods of sequence analysis are being tested successfully with the much smaller transport RNA which, as we shall discuss later, plays a key role in cellular protein synthesis. The hope appears justified that our knowledge about nucleic acid chemistry may accumulate according to the kinetics of a multi-hit curve (see Fig. 16) and that we are now getting close to the bend in Curve B, where the rate of decrease of our ignorance suddenly picks up steam.

The biological role
of viral components

THE ATTENTIVE READER
will by now have acquired a casual speaking acquaintance
with the chemistry of proteins and nucleic acids. This
should facilitate his understanding of the main topics of
this chapter, the mode of construction of a virus particle
and the respective biological roles of its two important
components.

When Stanley, in 1935, identified a definite physicochemical entity as the causative agent of the tobacco
mosaic disease, he initiated a new era in virus research,
which brought forth the detailed characterization of many
clearly defined disease-causing virus particles. This transfer
of viruses into the realm of the exact sciences of physics and
chemistry met with some prejudice and opposition, and
certain authors tried to muddy the waters by reporting observations to the effect that virus particles were not really
uniform in size; that they might grow like organisms; and
that the little fellows could cause the disease as well as the
"full-grown" particles. Such poorly substantiated claims
have recurred periodically, even as late as 1959. However,
when the waters of scientific progress flow rapidly like a
mountain stream, they do not stay muddied long. They do,
occasionally, cascade abruptly to a new level, and that is
what happened in virology during the years of 1955 and
1956, and what will now be described.

Several methods were known to degrade virus particles and separate the viral proteins from the nucleic acids. One method in particular, elaborated by Schramm and co-workers in Germany, permitted the isolation of native protein from TMV. By treatment of the virus with quite weak alkali (sodium hydroxide, pH 10.5) near 0°C, these authors obtained the protein in such a state that it retained its ability to aggregate under appropriate conditions, forming rods which looked and behaved pretty much like virus particles. Great must have been their disappointment when the virus-like particles were not infectious.

About the same time, Markham and Smith of Cambridge, England, made an important discovery while studying a new type of plant virus called turnip yellows mosaic (TYM). These authors obtained definite evidence that infected plant juice contained two kinds of spherical particles of identical size: one which contained RNA (about 37%) and was infective, and another which lacked the RNA and was noninfective. Similarly, virus-like noninfective protein fractions resembling TMV had been obtained from TMV-infected plant juice by Takahashi and others. It thus began to appear more and more probable that the protein gave the virus particles their typical shape but that the RNA was responsible for viral infectivity.

A series of important experiments performed by Hershey and Chase in 1952 had shown that upon infection of bacteria by bacteriophages almost only the phage DNA and hardly any of its protein entered the bacterium. Other evidence was at hand showing that pure DNA sufficed for the transmittal of genetic information from one bacterial strain to another (the so-called transforming principle first studied by Avery and McCarthy). But no genetic role had been established for the simpler RNA molecule. Actually, the fact that different strains of TMV were known to differ in their amino acid composition, but not in their nucleotide composition, supported the prevailing belief that in the simple RNA viruses the protein was actually the genetic component. By coincidence, most plant virus researchers were specialists in protein chemistry, which may have contributed to their prejudice. As an illustration, this author, upon joining the newly created virus laboratory at the University of California in 1952, initiated experiments in which he tried to produce viral mutants by modifying the amino acid sequence of the TMV protein through addition of amino acids to the chain ends, and none of his associates —virus chemists of longer standing, these—laughed at him or discouraged his efforts. Yet, as we have indicated, a few years later the stage was set, and it was time for a change.

The author was then frequently preparing the protein from TMV in denatured form suitable for chemical studies. For this purpose he degraded the virus by means of a detergent, sodium dodecyl sulfate (SDS). The nucleic acid fraction was usually thrown away. The protein so prepared was thoroughly denatured and had lost its ability to aggregate to rods, but native protein prepared by the weak-alkali method was also at hand, and one day he and his faithful assistant, Mrs. B. Singer, decided "just for fun," to allow that native protein to aggregate in the presence of some of the RNA obtained as a by-product in the detergent degradation of the virus. The presence of virus-like particles gives a solution a characteristic opalescence, and it seemed that the tube containing both RNA and protein became more opalescent than that containing protein alone. This suggested that the presence of the RNA favored the tendency of the protein to aggregate to rods. It seemed not impossible that the RNA actually entered into the rod formation and that complete nucleoprotein particles were re-formed under such conditions, rather than pure protein particles. Protein particles are noninfectious, but how about these hypothetical nucleoprotein particles? Well, for an experimentalist the delay is short between asking such a question and performing a test, and, thus, the same day this reaction mixture was rubbed onto a few leaves of some test tobacco plants. Three days later, the leaves receiving the reaction product of RNA and protein showed a few typical virus lesions, while none appeared on the leaves rubbed with similar amounts of pure protein or pure nucleic acid. It seemed that virus activity, abolished by degrading the particle to the level of its two components, was regenerated by allowing these to recombine. This reaction, which we termed virus reconstitution, has been studied in considerable detail ever since; it has been refined and put on a strictly quantitative basis; it has also been confirmed, and used, by many at first quite sceptical colleagues in various laboratories. We can now predict that from 5 mg of good TMV RNA and 95 mg of good TMV protein, we can obtain about 50 mg of virus (50% yield) which is indistinguishable, by all tests and criteria, from a good preparation of natural TMV.

Possibly the most straightforward technique for the study of a TMV preparation is electron microscopy. By this technique Dr. R. C. Williams showed that typical virus rods were formed upon reconstitution. Quantitative studies showed that the infectivity of a preparation was a direct function of its content in typical full-length (300 mμ) particles. Shorter rods, which were present to a varying extent, did not appear to contribute to the infectiousness of the preparation. One very striking observation appeared quite mysterious at the time of these experiments: no rods longer than 300 mμ were ever observed by Dr. Williams. What factor could account for this definite length limitation of virus particles?

Earlier studies of the aggregation of the protein alone had shown that it was able to form much longer rods, if the solution was made faintly acid (pH 5). These facts pointed to the RNA as the length-limiting factor; but since we, at that time, did not envision the RNA as a single long chain molecule, it was not clear to us how this effect could come about. On the basis of present knowledge, as summarized best by the model in Fig. 4, it is now quite self-evident that the length of the polynucleotide chain determines the length of the stable virus particle. For the nucleic acid must be fitted into a specific site or groove on each of the "co-centrically" aggregating protein units (see Fig. 18)* to

---

* See figures at end of book.

become at all accommodated. The cross-sectional diameter
of the RNA helix inside the protein helix is well known,
as is the pitch of the helix, and from these and the calculated extended length of a 6500 unit polynucleotide
chain, the length of the TMV rod can be derived by simple
arithmetic. This calculated value for the length of the
TMV particle is just about the same as that derived from
various physical properties over 20 years ago and beautifully
confirmed by direct measurements on electron micrographs
a few years later. It has even been possible to measure
directly the maximal length of the extended RNA thread
(about 3000 mμ) which was used in the above calculation
(Fig. 19).*

Thus, everything seems to fit together and gives us what
is probably a true understanding of the mechanism of *in
vivo* formation, as well as of *in vitro* reconstitution, of TMV
particles. The protein molecules moving about faster as
the temperature of the solution is raised, tend to stick to
one another when they collide in proper manner and thus
aggregate as shown in Fig. 18. In the presence of the RNA,
the protein tends to coaggregate with the RNA to give particles which become increasingly more stable as they proceed
to form, and each unit gets bonded to its 6 neighbors as
well as to the internal RNA chain. It thus becomes less
surprising that the particle, even though consisting of up to
95% protein, is considerably more resistant to disorganizing
influences, such as heat or enzymes, than the disaggregated
protein. It also now appears less surprising than it did in
1956 that a virus "made" *in vitro* (in the test tube) is just
as stable and just as infective as the natural virus, for both
are made in the same manner and by the same mechanism.

We will now continue the discussion of the revolution
that occurred in our concept of viruses in 1955–1956. The
reconstitution experiments had shown that an appreciable
fraction of the original virus infectivity was regenerated
as a consequence of the interaction of protein and RNA,
each of which at a hundred-fold higher concentration
showed little if any infectivity. The interpretation seemed

* See figures at end of book.

very obvious: infectivity is a property characteristic of the complete virus particle, requiring both components in structural unison. However, obvious interpretations of natural phenomena should always be looked at askance. In the present case, further work showed that the situation was a little more complex and, at the same time, much more interesting than first supposed. I stated above that the viral protein and RNA, each tested separately at relatively high concentrations, showed "little if any" infectivity. Now this is not a very scientific expression, for how little is little enough to be overlooked or disregarded? The protein usually produced no viral lesions even when tested at very high concentration, and thus passed the test. The RNA, on the other hand, usually did give a few lesions when freshly prepared and carefully applied. The amount of free RNA needed to produce disease symptoms was very much greater than of the same RNA when reconstituted with protein. But if the above interpretation were correct, then the RNA, alone, should be as dead or inert as the protein.

The simplest explanation of these observations was to attribute the small amount of infectivity remaining in the RNA fraction to the presence of a small amount of undegraded or incompletely degraded virus in that fraction. Chemists are usually quite content when they can separate two components so that each contains no more than 1% of the other, or of the starting material; and as little as 0.1% of virus remaining with the RNA could well have accounted for its residual infectivity. Contamination of the RNA with a trace of virus appeared to be a very reasonable explanation of a puzzling fact. Whether it also happened to be the right explanation could only be established by experiments. If this infectivity in the RNA was actually due to undegraded virus, then it would be expected to behave like the virus in all respects.

It is typical of the progress of science that the logical path we have here developed was taken independently and simultaneously both in our laboratory and in that of Professor

Schramm at Tübingen. After, and perhaps because of, my report on the reconstitution of active virus from its inactive components at the International Congress of Biochemistry at Brussels in 1955, the research efforts of both groups centered on the viral RNA. The German group, in particular H. Gierer, adopted a method for the isolation of RNA which had been previously employed by Kirby in England, and this method has proven most useful and convenient for the isolation of all kinds of viral RNA and is now in quite general use. It consists of stirring the virus with a mixture of phenol and water. The protein becomes denatured and dissolves in dissociated form in the water-saturated phenol layer, while the RNA remains dissolved in the water phase, the upper layer in a centrifuge tube. The RNA isolated by this procedure showed the same properties as that isolated by us after detergent degradation by means of salt fractionation, as it was used in the reconstitution studies. Both types of RNA preparations showed similarly low infectivity. Both research groups faced the problem of whether this infectivity was an intrinsic property of the RNA, or whether it was due to contamination by a small amount of virus. And so they went to work in this uncharted land, neither group knowing how close their research trail was to that of the other. Were this a land on earth, and not of the mind, then a hypothetical meeting similar to that which brought H. M. Stanley and Dr. Livingstone ("I presume") face-to-face in darkest Africa in 1887 could facetiously be invented.

The simplest and most clear-cut test which showed that the infectivity was due to the RNA and not to intact virus was supplied by experiments with the enzyme ribonuclease. This enzyme, produced in the pancreas of mammals for the purpose of degrading the RNA of foods, is of high specificity, which means that it attacks only RNA and products derived from RNA. Ribonuclease, however, is unable to get at the RNA of TMV and many other viruses, because they are protected by a well-fitting protein coat. Thus, TMV is not affected by this enzyme. Yet very small amounts of enzyme rapidly degraded and, at the same rate, abolished the infectivity of viral RNA preparations. These experiments certainly suggested very strongly that in bare RNA a new type of infectious material had been discovered.

Another obvious test is one aiming at the size or molecular weight of the infective principle. The rate of sedimentation in an ultracentrifuge is the simplest criterion of this property. The virus with its particle weight of 40 million (it weighs as much as 40 million hydrogen atoms) has a high sedimentation rate of about 180 S, while RNA with a molecular weight of 2 million sediments much more slowly in the centrifugal field (30 S in salt solutions, and about 5 S in water). When such tests were performed with infectious RNA, they clearly showed that the infective agent did not sediment like virus, nor even like partly degraded virus, but rather like RNA. The simplest way to perform such experiments was in a qualitative manner. Very high speed centrifugation was shown to remove added virus even in trace amounts from RNA solutions—the virus becoming stuck at the bottom of the tube. However, the infectivity occurring naturally in viral RNA was not sedimented to the bottom under these conditions.

Other tests which gave supporting evidence to the new concept of infectious RNA made use of differences in the salt precipitation properties of RNA and virus; others compared the stability of the two. The RNA is generally found to be much more labile than one might expect from its chemical structure, and this is regarded as due to its great susceptibility to attack by various enzymes and their ubiquitous occurrence. This has complicated all studies of the RNA. In particular, the interpretation of one type of test designed to differentiate virus infectivity from RNA infectivity, namely the serological, was jeopardized by this sensitivity of the RNA to enzymes. As is well known, the repeated injection of a proteinaceous material (the so-called antigen) into an animal, preferably a rabbit, leads to the appearance of antibodies in its blood serum. Such an antibody specifically combines with the antigen that caused its production. If the antigen was of bacterial or viral nature, the antibody usually inactivates the infective agent. This phenomenon is due to the interaction of two proteins specifically fitted to one another. Thus, in the serum of a rabbit immunized with TMV, there is an anti-TMV protein which binds and inactivates TMV but is not expected to inactivate TMV-RNA. Yet when such tests were performed, some loss of infectivity was also observed in RNA preparations. That this was not due to the specific reaction of anti-TMV with either the infective RNA or remaining traces of infectious virus, was shown when serum from nonimmunized rabbits was used as a control. This also caused loss of RNA infectivity, and the later demonstration of the presence of ribonuclease in rabbit and other sera provided an adequate explanation for all these observations.

It was necessary to perform so much elaborate work to establish the intrinsic infectivity of RNA and to remove the last doubts of the skeptics, because the RNA was of such unexpectedly low infectivity. This could, *a priori*, be attributed to extensive inactivation occurring in the course of virus degradation and isolation of the RNA. However, when the same RNA preparation upon reconstitution proved to be about 50% active, but upon direct assay only 0.1%, it seemed probable that its low direct infectivity was another consequence of its sensitivity to enzymes. For the host plant also is rich in a variety of RNA degrading enzymes, and the inoculation procedure, which includes rubbing the leaf surface with an abrasive (carborundum), may well contribute to the loss of most of the infective RNA before it can reach its field of action inside a surviving cell.

This interpretation is supported by a variety of observations. Thus, the relative infectivity of a given preparation of the RNA, as compared to that of intact or reconstituted virus, varies appreciably from test to test and, probably, also seasonally. The infectivity of the RNA is also very dependent on the age of the plant and the type of plant used. It is further quite dependent on the salt concentration in the inoculating medium. Finally, the addition of bentonite, an acidic silicate clay from the Rocky Mountain area, which is known to bind and inactivate ribonuclease (as well as other basic proteins) was found greatly to increase the relative infectivity of the RNA without affecting that of the intact virus. Thus, all indications are that the RNA is inactivated to a large and varying extent in the course of the assay. It has been the general custom at our laboratory to forestall this by testing the RNA, whenever possible, in the reconstituted form.

The facts and interpretations concerning the nature of infective RNA, as described above, are due largely to the two laboratories mentioned, but they have been supported by experiments in other laboratories and have become more or less generally accepted. There are, however, a few minority opinions. Before discussing those that have some factual basis, I would like to interject a short discussion of a topic which one might call researchman-ship, or how best to advance one's scientific career. One obviously advisable way is to make an original discovery or express an original idea. This is, however, neither easy nor certain to succeed. It is not easy for more than the one obvious reason that one may lack the necessary material; the other reason is that almost everything has been at least suggested, if not attempted, before. This leads to the cause for this path not necessarily being successful: the idea or discovery must be made at the right time, when the scientific community is ready for it. Otherwise, it will be overlooked or forgotten, until rediscovered 10 or 20 years later by a luckier investigator.

Another way to the top, almost always successful, is to publish a lot of papers or give many talks, preferably on a variety of unrelated topics and each accompanied by a news release. Publishing a lot may lead any scientist into publishing some errors, be they due to faulty experimentation or to premature interpretations. Is that dangerous in that the errors count against him? Far from it, for such publications will be rebutted and criticized, which means that the paper is referred to, and a counter-rebuttal supplies an additional publication without the need of additional data or thoughts. In short, if publishing a lot has been selected as the path to success, then quality or veracity hardly matter. A man endowed with some political astuteness and a sense of salesmanship can count on this path to make him a man of note, if not of notoriety. He may soon play his role on the wider stage of scientific power policy. This may fulfill his heart's desire, but it may also be of advantage for science as a whole, since it means his removal from the scene of publishing investigators. But, alas, others are only waiting to follow in his steps.

These few pointers regarding the ladder of success for the budding young investigator may appear cynical to some and in bad taste to others. But it seems necessary to point out occasionally that science and technology, the great new religions of the 20th century, have their share of charlatans and self-centered promoters, just as all earlier religions and all walks of life peopled by people. The fact that these pseudoscientists usually tend toward positions of administrative power frequently directs their energies into channels where they can effectively do much good. In this domain, they join and may adequately replace the many great scientists who regard it as a moral obligation to accept administrative and policy forming responsibilities, when, actually, they would be happier in their research and teaching laboratories.

We now return to remaining doubts concerning the chemical nature of the infective material in TMV-RNA preparations. If the RNA, as such, were not the active ingredient, then what other components are present in these preparations, and which of them could be implicated? One suggestion is that DNA, known to be the most common genetic determinant, might play this role also in TMV. This has been completely ruled out, for no DNA can be detected in TMV or in TMV-RNA preparations by the very sensitive methods now available for the detection of DNA. Other suggestions implicate protein, usually not as the prime active component, but as a necessary fellow traveler operating in conjunction with the RNA. Thus, if one peptide chain remained associated with each RNA molecule, this might carry the blueprints for protein replication into the infected cell. Other more fantastic theories will not be mentioned, but this one requires consideration. The following facts prove it erroneous. On chemical grounds, amino acid analyses show that good TMV RNA contains no more than about 0.05% of protein. By using virus labelled in its protein moiety with radioactive sulfur (S^{35}), it was possible to show that the best preparations of RNA made in the presence of bentonite, the enzyme-binding clay, contained only enough sulfur for 0.02–0.04% of TMV protein. This would suffice for only one peptide chain per 25–50 molecules of the RNA, but actually it appears probable that this small residual amount of radioactive sulfur is not really indicative of the presence of viral protein but is due to traces of plant proteins, peptides, enzymes, etc.

Subsequent experiments with the sulfur labelled RNA showed that upon reconstitution the last traces of protein were further reduced, being displaced by the added "cold" (unlabelled) protein. This is important in considering the biological evidence against the theory that a trace of virus protein might play an important genetic function in the RNA induced virus replication.

The biological evidence is based on experiments in which RNA and protein isolated from different strains of TMV were combined and reconstituted. Let us call the two strains simply A and B, and let us reconstitute protein from strain A with nucleic acid from strain B (Fig. 20).* The reconstituted virus then shows the expected mixed character: the nature of the disease is characteristic for strain B (the donor of the RNA), but antibody to strain A (the source of the protein) selectively inhibits its infectivity by the typical serological protein reaction. This artificially prepared mixed virus is then allowed to replicate, and the progeny virus is isolated in bulk. Analysis of its protein in terms of amino acid composition clearly shows that it is

* See figures at end of book.

indistinguishable from strain B, the "parent" which donated the RNA. Thus, the chemical evidence that RNA can be freed from detectable amounts of its own protein is supported by the genetic evidence that, even if the hypothetical last remaining traces of that protein are replaced by another protein, the genetic activity of the RNA is neither impaired nor confused. The RNA of a given strain of virus can and does evoke the production of more virus of that same strain. It carries all the information required for its replication and for the production of its characteristic protein, and it needs no traces of accompanying protein to assist it in its task.

This new concept of the genetic activity and supremacy of viral RNA has been more and more firmly established since it was first proclaimed for TMV in 1956. Intrinsic infectivity has since been demonstrated for the RNA of many viruses from bacterial, plant, and animal sources, including the polio virus, and in all cases where this was investigated, the RNA seemed to carry the complete genetic information, although this has not generally been as firmly established as with TMV. Some bigger and more complex RNA viruses have not yet yielded their RNA in infectious form. On the other hand, from the simplest DNA viruses, the small bacteriophages, infective nucleic acid has recently been isolated in several laboratories.

We have summarized the evidence that as complex a biological phenomenon as that of inheritance can be attributed to as comparatively simple a molecule as a polynucleotide chain. This discovery has stimulated a considerable amount of both research and thinking along new lines. It seems probable that RNA as such, or possibly in some lightly encased and protected form, may spread from cell to cell and thus propagate a virus disease. It has also been suggested that RNA may play this role of transmitting genetic information from cell to cell in pathological states which are not identified or characterized by the appearance of a typical virus particle. It is quite possible that cellular genetic aberrations of the kind we call malignancy or cancer may be spread in such a manner. It is much too early to attempt an evaluation of the impact on general biology due to the recognition of the biological potential of viral RNA. However, it seems certain that this realization makes RNA a material of greatest biological interest, and that it behooves the chemist to learn as much as possible about its structure and its mode of function, and to develop new methods which will lead him further. Some of the general principles of nucleic acid chemistry have been described in a previous chapter. We will now describe some of the current lines of chemical research as applied to the biologically active RNA molecule.

Let us start out with the now generally accepted premise, that a certain sequential arrangement of 6500 nucleotides represents the code which describes a given strain or type of the virus under investigation. One might then ask: What would happen if one altered the chemical structure of one, several, or many of the nucleotides along the chain? Most of the chemical alterations which are now possible consist of replacing hydrogen atoms on the bases by other groups, such as $-CH_3$ (methyl), $-CH_2CH_3$ (ethyl), $-Br$ (bromine), $-CH_2COOH$ (carboxymethyl), or $-CH_2CH_2OH$ (hydroxyethyl). If one regards the four nucleotides as letters of the genetic script, then one would expect such substitutions to "mess up" the letters and thus make the script less readable or completely undecipherable. The actually observed result is what one would expect: the introduction into an RNA molecule of one or two substituents of any of those listed above causes it to become unintelligible to the host and thus inactive as an infective agent. This is best shown by using radioactively labelled reagents, so that as small an extent of substitution as that involving one or two out of the 6500 nucleotides can be determined. It is also in this manner possible to detect which type of nucleotide is preferentially attacked and altered by a given reagent. Toward many reagents, guanine is most susceptible; for others, it is the cytosine.

While all reagents that combine with RNA lead to inactivation, a few produce additional effects which are considerably more interesting, and some are quite exciting. When the substituent is small, such as —CH$_3$ or —Br, then a very small fraction of the altered molecules may retain the ability to replicate. These, however, being different, often replicate abnormally, and the result is a mutant—a new strain of the virus. The same kind of result has also been obtained with DNA, whether the odd base was chemically produced or was incorporated into the DNA by the cell that synthesized it. As an example of this, 5-bromouracil is sufficiently similar to thymine (its —Br group replaces the —CH$_3$ group of thymine), to become incorporated in its stead into bacteriophage DNA, if the host bacteria are grown in a medium rich in bromouracil. However, during the replication of this bromouracil containing DNA, mutants are noted, which are attributed to occasional confusion and error in the replication of this almost-and-yet-not-quite thymine-like base. Thus, most bromouracils will pair with adenine and reappear as thymine after the next pairing, the damage thus being undone. An occasional bromouracil, however, will pair erroneously with guanine and thus become cytosine in the next generation. A new base sequence is now established, and the progeny of this molecule will be a mutant (see Fig. 21).

Similarly, the chemical introduction of small substituents into RNA is believed to occasionally confuse the replication mechanism and thus lead to mutants. Bigger substituent groups (such as the last ones of those listed on p. 88), on the other hand, which make the base quite unlike any natural base, completely confound the replication mechanism and therefore produce no mutants, but only inactive molecules.

We now come to one particular chemical modification reaction of RNA which differs from all others in an important respect. When one treats an amino compound with nitrous acid, the amino group becomes replaced by an hydroxyl group. This well-known deamination reaction was found to have remarkable effects when applied to RNA. The chemists (Schuster and Schramm) first established fa-

                                                                    ↓
(a)   A p T p G p T p A p G p C p T p T p T p A p T p G p T p C p C p A p G p C p
(b)   A p BU p G p T p A p G p C p T p T p BU p C p C p A p G p C p
(b¹) T   A   C   A   T   C   G   A   A   G   T   A   C   A   G   G   T   C   G
(c)   A p T p G p T p A p G p C p T p T p C p A p T p G p T p C p C p A p G p C

FIG. 21. *Illustration of the mechanism of mutation due to a base analog (or derivative). Line (a): A segment of a DNA chain; each letter represents a deoxynucleotide of adenine (A), thymine (T), cytosine (C), or guanine (G). When bacteria are grown in a medium rich in 5-bromouracil (BU) and deficient in thymine, some of the former is introduced into newly synthesized DNA in place of thymine (line b). Upon base pairing of this modified DNA strand (b) (in a normal BU free medium) some of the BU pairs with A, but an occasional one pairs with G (line b¹). Base pairing of b¹, completing the replication cycle (c), reproduces the original sequence (a), except for the occasional error (T→BU→G→C), which represents a spot mutation.*

vorable conditions and demonstrated that the reaction
achieved the expected transformation of the three amino
bases (adenine, guanine, and cytosine) to the corresponding
hydroxy bases (hypoxanthine, xanthine, and uracil). But
here one must sit up and take notice—one of these changes
represents the direct transformation of one regular RNA
component into another, for cytosine is transformed to
uracil.

Cytosine   ⟶   Uracil

If each letter in the genetic script carries information, then
one would expect that a change of one letter to another in
the same script would infallibly result in a changed message, or, in biological terms, such a change should always
produce a mutant. And this seems to be the case, for
Gierer and Mundry discovered, and others have amply confirmed, that nitrous acid is a remarkable mutagen. After
deamination, which, like all other reactions, causes loss of
infectivity in most molecules, an astonishingly high inci-
dence of mutants can be observed among the surviving
molecules. When about 90–99% of the infectivity is abolished, the "surviving molecules" are at least 70%, and possibly nearly 100% mutants, each polynucleotide chain probably unlike the other. This is quite dramatically different
from all other mutagenic agents or effects. Deamination of
RNA is the only presently known reaction which transforms
one component base into another (cytosine → uracil), and
it seems very likely that this reaction is so highly mutagenic for just this reason. The other deaminations, including that of cytosine as it occurs in DNA, would be pre-

dominantly inactivating and only rarely mutagenic, since their reaction products would be bases foreign to the nucleic acids, similar to the methyl and bromine derivatives discussed above.

We have discussed some of the author's current ideas on the production of mutants. But such hypothetical schemes have little definite meaning unless considered in conjunction with a particular replication mechanism, as was done in Fig. 21. For that purpose we must refer the reader back to the earlier discussion of the Watson and Crick structure of DNA and the mechanism proposed for the replication of DNA. It seems that we are stuck with that concept of pairs of complementary bases, each, through its hydrogen-bonding affinity, searching out what might be called its chemical mate. No other mechanisms have been proposed which can express the replication of a polynucleotide chain in chemically sense-making terms. And although there is less evidence that this mechanism is operative for RNA than for DNA, it has been generally accepted as the best working hypothesis available. All we have to do when considering RNA is to replace thymine by uracil; the H-bonding fit of uracil to adenine is as good as that of its 5-methyl derivative, thymine, as shown in Fig. 10. According to recent studies with model compounds, furthermore, it appears probable that a single strand of DNA can direct the synthesis of a complementary RNA strand by the usual pairing mechanism, and indications have been obtained that the two can occur in nature in the form of a joint double-stranded helix.

Thus, to return to the mutagenic actions of nitrous acid, deamination of one cytosine to a uracil will make that RNA chain bind a complementary adenine instead of a guanine at that spot. The chemical change has directly mutated the molecule, and it will now replicate in this new form. In contrast, reactions such as the introduction of a methyl group on the 1 or 3 position of a purine are probably always inactivating, because they interfere with base pairing. On the other hand, a methyl group on the 7-position of guanine may only occasionally cause an erroneous binding of uracil instead of cytosine, and thus an occasional mutant arises in the course of replication. The bromination of a pyrimidine might have a similar hit-or-miss effect, as illustrated in Fig. 21.

Mutation has been the subject of discussion for quite a while, without any explanation of what we mean by a mutant, or how we detect it. But better late than never. A mutant of a virus, which is synonymous with a strain or variant, is usually detected, because it gives a different disease symptom on the host. Since many different varieties of tobacco as well as many other plant species are affected by TMV, and most of them react in a different manner to the common TMV (often called the wild-type by geneticists), the chance of detecting a mutant character is largely a function of the number of different hosts tested. A given mutant may give symptoms which are not distinguishable from those of common TMV on the first five host varieties tested; if on the sixth it gives a different symptom, and if it does so infallibly on that host, then that test sets it apart as a mutant. The symptoms one looks out for belong usually to either of two main classes: the virus spreads throughout the plant (systemic disease), or it remains confined to the leaf area which was inoculated (local lesions, see Fig. 2). A great variety of symptoms is possible when the disease is systemic, often called by such descriptive terms as blistering, mosaic, ring-spot, yellow, and mottled. The absence of noticeable symptoms is one extreme, and the killing of the plant the other extreme in the range of severity or virulence of TMV mutants when acting on Turkish tobacco. In regard to the local lesion response, we have shown a leaf in the earlier figure that carried very different lesions on its two halves. The small ones were actually produced by one of our nitrous acid mutants, although many mutants are not distinguishable from the wild type by the appearance of their local lesions.

The foregoing may suffice to give the reader a feeling for

the variety of biological effects that one can survey in the search for mutants of a plant virus. In similar manner, differences in the appearance of viral plaques on tissue culture or bacterial plates permit the detection of mutants of animal and bacterial viruses. A great number of mutants have been detected by the above methods after chemical modification of TMV RNA. However, we have also repeatedly observed mutants which differed from common TMV in the same manner, or, in other words, which did not differ from one another. Too little is known about these phenomena to permit definite interpretations, but it seems possible that certain preferred mutants reappear frequently, even when different mutagenic agents are employed for their evocation. By the same token, it seems probable that some mutants remain undetected, because their symptoms, on the hosts used, are not distinguishably different from those given by common TMV. This may only mean that the host that would differentiate these seemingly identical mutants has not yet been found.

Such uncertainties in classifying mutants illustrate the need for additional, and different approaches to their study. Fortunately, several independent methods are available. One of these which plays an important role in the classification of pathogenic virus strains, such as those of the flu virus, makes use of their serological differences which are a consequence of the differences in the viral proteins. Another method used extensively with TMV focuses attention directly on the viral protein. We have previously mentioned that the proteins of most natural strains of TMV differ from one another in their amino acid composition (Table I). It thus is apparent that the amino acid composition of chemically produced mutants is of greatest interest. If differences in composition were detected, this would supply a chemical means of identifying and differentiating numerous mutants.

Current studies along these lines have given very interesting results. Several mutants produced by one or the other of the chemical agents discussed above were selected on the basis of showing a marked biological change, for they produced local lesions on a variety of tobacco which reacts in systemic manner to common-TMV. Each of these, upon amino acid analysis, showed an exchange of one to three amino acid residues. In contrast, several mutants studied by Wittmann in Tübingen, and others studied by us, which only differed from common TMV in giving milder systemic symptoms on Turkish tobacco, showed no or only one difference in amino acid composition from that virus. It would seem that changes in the protein are not a necessary, but a sufficient and very selective, criterion for the detection, differentiation, and classification of mutants. The observation that certain exchanges recurred quite frequently (for instance, ser → phe, pro → leu), but that their reversal as well as many others never did, became understandable when we began to learn some of the secrets of the genetic code, a topic we will discuss in the next chapter. Thus the study of protein changes resulting from chemical modification of viral RNA brought us closer to the final goal, a comprehension of the chemical mechanism involved in genetic information transfer.

How soon will this aim be reached? Unfortunately, not for quite a while. The main hurdles in the path toward a complete understanding of the genetic activity of RNA are the need for knowledge of the complete chemical structure of both the protein "products" and the RNA "producer." As far as the protein goes, we know the complete structure of the coat protein of TMV (Fig. 9), but there may exist other proteinaceous products not yet isolated from the infected cell, such as new enzymes arising as intermediates in the production of the virus. The real bottleneck, however, is the chemical elucidation of long nucleotide sequences and the location of the mutational change, or in simpler words: when will we be able to say that, in a given mutant produced by nitrous acid, a cytosine in position 4927 along the chain has been replaced by uracil? This, unfortunately, is many years away. For research on the elucidation of long nucleotide sequences has barely begun, and new methods need to be developed for this difficult task.

In contrast, such specific information is now beginning to become available for the coat protein of TMV. For, in mutants which differ in amino acid composition, it begins to be possible to pinpoint the difference on the amino acid sequence map. This was first achieved with a nitrous acid mutant through the lucky coincidence that a change had occurred near the end of the protein chain. We have previously discussed the nature of the C-terminal group of the peptide chain and the presumed reason why the enzyme carboxypeptidase splits off only the terminal threonine (p. 44). This was attributed to the proline in the third position, which prevents further attachment and attack by the enzyme, for which an —NH—CO— group is required beyond the one to be split (see Fig. 22). When the first chemically evoked mutant to be analyzed (#171, see Table I) contained one proline less than did common TMV, it seemed worth while to Tsugita, a guest researcher from Japan at our laboratory, to see what carboxypeptidase would do to this virus protein. And this curiosity was well rewarded. The enzyme did an astonishing lot, splitting off threonine, then alanine, then leucine, and gradually 13 more residues along the chain. Thus, the first change was located; the third residue from the C-terminus was leucine instead of proline (R''' in our schematic presentation was thus replaced). Other replacements must be more laboriously located by first splitting the mutant protein into its component peptides with trypsin, then finding which peptide differs in composition, and finally analyzing this peptide sequentially to locate the position of the exchange. Such work is in progress, and several changes have already been located.

When a basic amino acid, such as arginine or lysine, is lost or gained by mutation, this means one less or one more place for trypsin to attack, and thus a different pattern of peptides which may be detected with relative ease. This principle was utilized in an ingenious manner by Wittmann.

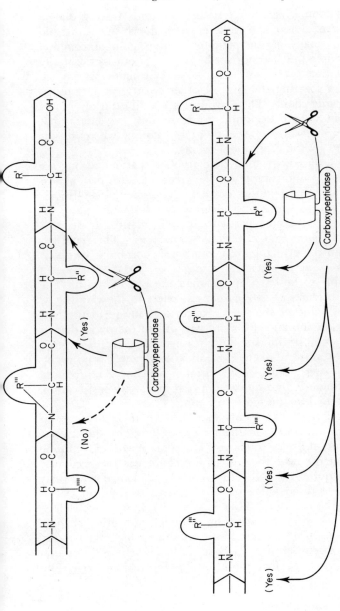

FIG. 22. Attack of carboxypeptidase on two peptide chains. Top: A chain which, like TMV protein, has proline (R''') as the third residue from the carboxyl end, which prohibits a second attachment of the enzyme after the terminal residue (R' = threonine) has been released by the enzyme. Bottom: A chain lacking proline, from which many amino acids are successively split off (in strain 171, see text; R''' would be leucine).

For by comparing several natural mutants lacking one of their basic amino acid residues, he deduced the sequential order of many of the peptides in the chain of common TMV when this had not yet been worked out by the standard methods previously discussed. Wittmann also is engaged in locating the sites of other natural mutations on the peptide chain. These are just a few illustrations of the fact that we are beginning to know our way about that protein molecule, to the point of finding where it was wronged by the mutational event.

The terminology used here implies that mutations are regarded as unfavorable for the virus, and this may almost always be the case under normal environmental conditions. The common strain of a virus *is* that common strain, because it has become particularly well adapted to its task through innumerable selection processes. This concept, based on the principles of evolution, is borne out by observations of many chemical mutants of TMV which seem invariably to be less virulent than the parent strain. The term virulence, as here employed, refers to the viability or survival value of the virus. As far as damage to the host goes, many mutants are more harmful to the plant than is the common strain. But since survival of a virus is dependent upon survival of the host, its killing power is no evolutionary asset. Thus, those variants which are reproduced most copiously by a flourishing host may, with justification, be regarded as the most virulent.

How mutational events may achieve their detrimental effect is illustrated on the molecular level by the nitrous acid mutant discussed above. The replacement of a proline by a leucine near the end of the chain has rendered that mutant quite susceptible to an enzyme, a change which may well be as disadvantageous to the virus in the host cell as it is in the test tube. Thus, it seems likely that this change represents an evolutionary impediment, and other changes might produce the same result for similar or other reasons.

This discussion may lead the reader to believe that mutation is a waste, since evolution has resulted in perfection.

While this may be often true under standard conditions, it must be remembered, however, that mutation plays the important role of enabling an organism to adapt itself to changed circumstances. Thus, the introduction of penicillin has seriously threatened many bacterial populations, and it was only those otherwise possibly inferior mutants that happened to be able to cope with this bacterial poison, and to save the species and to give it time to again perfectly adapt itself, through mutation and selection, to its new penicillinous environment. Similarly, it may happen that a mutation toward higher radiation resistance may enable a subspecies of *Homo,* quite possibly non-*sapiens,* to survive alone into the twenty-first century.

Chemical mechanism
of replication

WE HAVE COME TO KNOW A little about the chemical nature of the two important components of viruses, the protein and the nucleic acid. We have seen some of the evidence which shows that the base sequence of the nucleic acids of viruses carries detailed genetic information. We have seen that, in the cell it invades, the nucleic initiates far-reaching metabolic events leading to its own reproduction as well as of that of its coat protein. Do we have any ideas about the mechanisms of these processes? The answer to this is a qualified yes. Until recently we had nothing but speculations, sometimes called theories by their proponents. But thanks to the exciting work by Kornberg and others on the synthesis of DNA and RNA, we now begin to have a means of studying nucleic acid replication in a system considerably less complex than the living cell. The main features of these important studies are as follows:

All life processes require the presence of macromolecules, such as proteins and nucleic acids, and these must be built up from smaller molecules by chemical processes which require energy. A chemist supplies energy to his reactions by such tricks as boiling the mixture on a hot plate, but biological materials are adapted to operate within a limited temperature range and lose their structure and activity at high temperatures. The trick Nature uses is to load its intermediate chemical agents with extra chemical energy to make them directly operative. Such potential chemical energy, similar in principle to that of a charged battery, enables the living cell to function. The same principle can also be employed by the biochemist who wants to perform biological reactions *in vitro*, i.e., in the test tube. Thus, if one wants to synthesize nucleic acid, one must first get the nucleotides, the building blocks, into an activated form. The form used by biological systems is to attach pyrophosphate groups to the 5′ nucleotides. The anhydride forms of acids (two acids condensed, with loss of water) are quite generally very reactive, one might say "charged" molecules. Many of them react readily in various ways and hydrolyze spontaneously in water at low temperature. To illustrate the principle, two anhydrides commonly used by the organic chemist (a,b), and two of great biological significance (c,d) are shown on p. 102. In the case of the pyrophosphate linkage, which represents an anhydride form of phosphoric acid (d), hydrolysis occurs sufficiently slowly to make this type of compound an enormously useful biological energy reservoir.

The corresponding triphosphates of the four deoxynucleosides which make up DNA have been prepared, and these represent the logical building-blocks-plus-built-in-energy to synthesize DNA. The other important ingredient is a biological catalyst, or an enzyme. Such enzymes can be isolated from a variety of cells or tissues. Kornberg used mainly an enzyme from a bacterium (*Escherichia coli*). A third important ingredient in this, as in many other enzyme-catalyzed reactions, is a divalent metal ion such as magnesium (Mg^{++}). This probably serves to bring enzyme and substrate closer together. The mixture of enzyme, magnesium, and two compounds of the above type, for instance, the triphosphates of deoxyadenosine and thymidine, will make an interesting double-stranded polymer resembling DNA in certain respects. But it obviously can't make DNA, since it lacks two of the four building blocks. Even with all four of these, however, nothing much happens unless

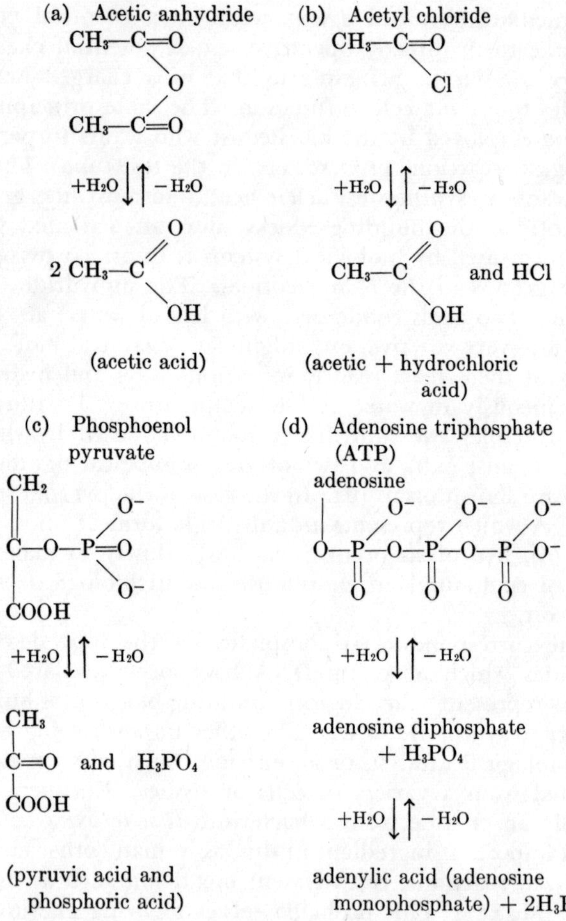

(a)   Acetic anhydride

$$CH_3—C{=}O$$
$$\diagdown$$
$$O$$
$$CH_3—C{=}O$$

$+H_2O \downarrow \uparrow -H_2O$

$$2\ CH_3—C\diagup^{O}_{\diagdown OH}$$

(acetic acid)

(b)   Acetyl chloride

$$CH_3—C{=}O$$
$$\diagdown$$
$$Cl$$

$+H_2O \downarrow \uparrow -H_2O$

$$CH_3—C\diagup^{O}_{\diagdown OH} \quad \text{and HCl}$$

(acetic + hydrochloric acid)

(c)   Phosphoenol pyruvate

$$CH_2$$
$$\|$$
$$C—O—P{=}O$$
$$| \qquad\qquad$$
$$COOH$$

with O^- groups on P

$+H_2O \downarrow \uparrow -H_2O$

$$CH_3$$
$$|$$
$$C{=}O \quad \text{and} \quad H_3PO_4$$
$$|$$
$$COOH$$

(pyruvic acid and phosphoric acid)

(d)   Adenosine triphosphate (ATP)

adenosine

$$O—P—O—P—O—P—O^-$$

with O^- above and O below each P

$+H_2O \downarrow \uparrow -H_2O$

adenosine diphosphate $+ H_3PO_4$

$+H_2O \downarrow \uparrow -H_2O$

adenylic acid (adenosine monophosphate) $+ 2H_3PO_4$

another important ingredient is present, and that is a little DNA. This so-called primer DNA fulfills a most extraordinary and significant function which greatly transcends the meaning of the word "primer." It not only starts the enzymatic production of DNA, but it determines the nature of the product. It seems almost certain that the DNA produced by the enzyme is a replica of the DNA used as primer. This is quite different from all other enzyme reactions, in which the enzyme is specific in its operation and it alone determines the nature of the product. In the case of DNA synthesis it is the primer, not the enzyme, that determines what is being made. How the DNA manages to do this is not exactly known. The base pairing tendency of the polynucleotide chain surely represents the chemical basis of this replication. In line with this, single-stranded DNA is the best primer. The fact that now we can observe molecular replication to proceed in this simple system in solution is certainly going to be of enormous advantage when it comes to proving the actual reaction mechanism of this crucial biological phenomenon. It seems a thrill to be alive in an era when outer space becomes accessible to man; but at least as exciting, it seems to me, is a time in which macromolecules related to genes are observed to reproduce themselves in cell-free systems.

Less is known about RNA synthesis, although it has recently been shown to proceed by a very similar mechanism. It thus seems possible that the replication of the nucleic acid portion of all viruses may take place in such automatic and direct fashion. What makes it difficult to demonstrate this *in vitro* is the great sensitivity of the nucleic acids to the many enzymes which tend to degrade them and which are not easily separated from the synthesizing enzymes. *In vivo,* that is, in the cell, synthesis is probably favored by taking place in a compartment to which degradative enzymes have no admittance. It has been suggested that this occurs in the cell nucleus, and it seems certain that triphosphates are synthesized and utilized by the cell, as they are by the chemists in their *in vitro* system.

However, we must not forget that viruses consist largely of proteins, and concerning the mechanism by which nucleic acids dictate the synthesis of proteins, we have as yet nothing but educated guesses and speculations. Many authors believe that the virus-infected cell is at first forced into making new enzyme proteins, which in turn produce virus protein. Production of DNA has also been postulated as a necessary intermediate. There is no doubt that infection by the so-called T-even bacteriophages elicits new enzymes such as the ones required for the production of the odd nucleoside hydroxymethylcytidine, which the bacterium normally does not make at all. The invading DNA may at first, through base pairing, produce special complementary RNA chains, and the RNA molecules, in turn, are presumed to produce the various proteins by a mechanism which is

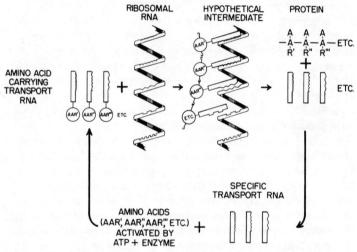

FIG. 23. *Partly hypothetical scheme of the mechanism of protein synthesis. For explanation see text. AAR', AAR", etc., represent different amino acids; the different saw edges represent different nucleotide sequences.*

now beginning to become clear. Many research teams are engaged in this very active field of protein synthesis, and the predominant ideas have been lucidly summarized by Hoagland and others. The principal facts illustrated in schematic fashion in Fig. 23 may be presented as follows:

The cytoplasm of all cells contains a set of relatively small RNA molecules, about 40–80 nucleotides long, which have been called transport RNA. Through the help of a specific enzyme, each RNA is able to bind a specific amino acid, which was previously put into an activated form by condensing it in anhydride fashion with a phosphate compound (ATP). As the result of this reaction we have about 20 different nucleotide sequences of transport RNA, each terminating in the identical trinucleotide sequence, with the terminal adenosine 3′ —OH group bound by ester linkage to a particular amino acid, as illustrated in the customary schematic representation shown below. The resultant

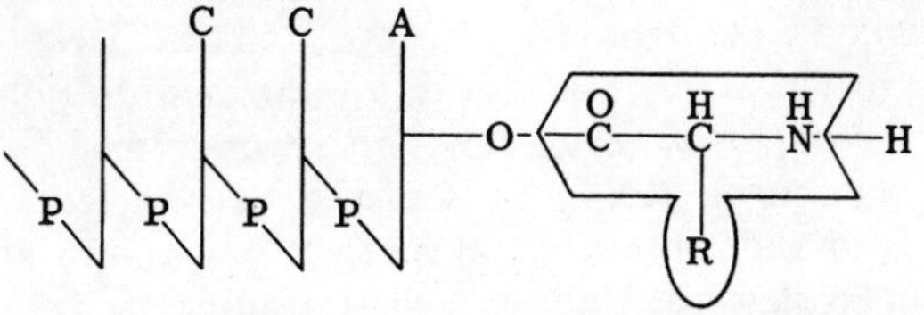

ester linkage is still of sufficiently high energy to react further, which is of great subsequent importance.

The following steps in the proposed mechanism of protein synthesis are based less firmly on fact, but the theories are appealing and no better ones are available. It is postulated that many of these relatively short nucleotide chains are bound by their base-pairing affinity to complementary base sequences in sequential order along the template RNA, the long polynucleotide chain which presumably is pressed out of the gene-DNA mold by base-pairing. These are located in the ribosomes, somewhat virus-like RNA-protein particles occurring in the cytoplasm of all cells. And then, in some as yet mysterious manner, the amino acids which are carried by the transport RNA segments and have thus also become aligned sequentially, let go of the RNA and interact with their neighbor, thus forming a peptide chain, and the protein is born (see Fig. 23). This fascinating concept may well be extensively modified in coming years, for several inconsistencies remain to be explained. But to have a mental image is better than to have none, and it is here presented (most superficially) in that spirit.

A great breakthrough on this front of our knowledge occurred during the second half of 1961, so that now we have some definite information on the relationship between RNA and protein to replace or support our previous guesses. It has become evident in recent years that the information carried by the DNA of genes is first transmitted to a short-lived kind of RNA. This is accomplished by base pairing, for it has become clear that the bases of a DNA chain pair as readily with the homologous ribonucleotides as with the deoxyribonucleotides (deoxyA...T or deoxyA...U, deoxy-G...deoxyC or deoxyG...C, etc.). Thus DNA is now known to act as primer also in ribonucleotide polymerization, creating *in vitro* an RNA in its own image. This so-called messenger RNA, in some as yet unclear manner, enters into the ribosome-transport RNA-protein synthesizing process described above and transmits the information from the gene-DNA, spelling out the amino acid sequence of the protein to be made. The ribosomes thus are reduced to the role of the production line. All this sounds pretty fantastic, and I have hesitated discussing these ideas, for they were derived from very complex evidence, the gaps in which were bridged by imagination. However, this has changed thanks to a remarkable discovery made recently by Nirenberg and Matthei of the National Institutes of Health, and to others.

These authors studied extracts from *E. coli* bacilli that contained ribosomes, transport RNA, and an energy supplying system (ATP, etc.), and they found, like everybody else, that this mixture could polymerize amino acids or incorporate them into proteins. But they made the new observation that the addition of big-molecular RNA led to great increases in the amount of amino acids incorporated by this system. Viral RNA worked very well, and the question naturally arose: what was the nature of the proteins synthesized under the stimulus of a particular viral RNA. To test this with TMV-RNA Nirenberg initiated a cooperative research project with our laboratory, while the effect of a coli bacteriophage RNA on this system was studied a year later by Zinder and others at the Rockefeller Institute. It seems that the protein made by the coli enzyme system, when primed by the coli phage RNA, is really largely the coat protein of the bacterial virus. However, our first impression that the *E. coli* extracts under the influence of TMV-RNA made something resembling TMV protein was not supported by later and more critical tests. An active research program is devoted to elucidate the reason for this failure. It could amount to differences in the dialects and thus in the transliteration of the genetic language of plant-adapted and bacteria-adapted RNA. But other explanations must also be considered which could account for the garbling of the TMV-RNA message by the bacterial system.

The other observation made by Nirenberg and Matthei has initiated a great advance in our understanding of the coding problem. For they found that their system responded not only to added RNA, but also to a simplified analog of RNA, a polymer of uridylic acid [poly-U, or $pUp(UpUp)_xU$]. But this polymer did not stimulate the incorporation of all amino acids, as did complete RNA. Poly-U caused the polymerization only of phenylalanine. For several years many famous mathematicians, physicists, and others had amused themselves in proposing coding theories to explain the relationship of the about 20 amino acids to the 4 nucleotides, always starting out by disproving the preceding theory and often ending up by disproving their own. Now for the first time a fact was at hand: Some number, probably three, of uridylic acid residues in the polymer chain somehow signified a phenylalanine residue. On the basis of this discovery many other polymers and copolymers (containing several nucleotides in various proportions) were tested for their specific effect of stimulating the polymerization of amino acids. It appeared that polycytidylic acid caused only proline to be incorporated in big molecular aggregates, while polyadenylic acid acted on lysine and the incorporation of all other amino acids could be attributed to the directing influence of various pairs or more probably triplets of mixed nucleotides. Since 64 triplet combinations of the 4 genetic letters [A, G, U (or T) and C] are possible, one might predict that each of the 20 amino acids could be coded for by several nucleotide triplets and this has turned out to be the case.

When the amino acid exchanges in TMV-protein which were observed in mutants produced by deamination of TMV-RNA, and which were discussed in the previous chapter, are compared with these code words, the agreement is in most instances rather remarkable. Thus, now that we know that phenylalanine is coded by poly-U, we can predict that phenylalanine could result from RNA deaminations (most of which are probably $C \to U$), but phenylalanine could never be replaced by another amino acid as a consequence of this reaction. On the other hand proline should be easily lost (CCC going to CCU, CUC, or UCC), but should never be formed as a consequence of deamination. This and several other predictions derived from a beginning understanding of the nature of the code have been borne out by the observations made in previous years. But occasionally these different sets of data do not jibe and then the researchers may have to walk the tight-rope across alibis, explanations, and embarrassment to a new level of recognition and understanding. But regardless of how smooth or rough may be the path of the investigator in this field, it always advances him towards his goal of explaining so-called life processes in terms of known physical and chemical laws.

Conclusions

THIS LITTLE BOOK CONTAINS
a fair amount of factual information. Because viruses consist of proteins and nucleic acids, it seemed essential to discuss the principles of protein and nucleic acid chemistry.
This supplied the groundwork from which specific question concerning the structure and function of viruses could
be approached. The principles of some modern biochemical methods and techniques were also touched upon. Wher-
ever possible, structure was related to biological function.
Also discussed was the manner in which logical deduction
determines the trail of research and leads from experiment
to experiment and often from conclusion to conclusion. A
summary of all this would be tiresome for the reader and
not very instructive for the browser and the skimmer of
pages. The principal conclusions, however, might be re-
stated as follows:

The simplest viruses, possibly the more primitive in
evolutionary terms, consist of RNA (ribonucleic acid) and
protein, and it is these that most of the discussion was about,
since more is known about their structure than about that
of the usually bigger and more complex DNA (deoxyribonucleic acid) containing viruses. Both classes carry the
nucleic acid encased in protein. In both, the protein plays,
primarily or entirely, a packaging and transport role, while
the nucleic acid is the active ingredient. The activity of a
virus, or its nucleic acid, lies in its ability to enter a living
cell, be it plant, animal, or bacterium, and force that cell

into a new alien metabolic pathway. For that cell now becomes harnessed into producing primarily virus constituents, instead of cell constituents. While the energy and the building materials for this synthetic work are supplied by the metabolism of the host cell, the blueprints describing the finished product, the virus, are supplied only by the invading viral nucleic acid. Thus the nucleic acid, RNA or DNA as the case may be, carries all the information necessary to make more of the viral nucleic acid, as well as of the one or several virus-specific proteins. This information is believed to be a function of the sequential arrangement of 4 generally different bases strung out along the polynucleotide chains of 6000 to 20,000 or more members.

Methods were discussed by which one can change the genetic message through chemical alteration of one or very few bases of a nucleic acid molecule, and thus produce mutants of the virus. Current concepts concerning the chemical mechanism of replication were touched upon briefly. Of particular fascination appears the evidence which shows that different nucleic acids may be replicated by the same enzyme. In the light of this it seems that there remains no fundamental gap in our understanding of viral replication. A nucleic acid can "take over" the synthetic apparatus *in vitro,* and by the same token it presumably can do so also in the cell that it invades. If the cell were needed only to supply the activated substrate and the polymerizing enzymes, then one would expect that it would soon become possible to synthesize viruses in *in vitro* systems. However, it appears probable that for the synthesis of the proteins, and for the protection of the newly made viral nucleic acid, structural elements such as the compartmentalization of the cell play an important role which cannot yet be duplicated *in vitro.* Once both components are finished, they combine readily into the typical particles. This phase of virus production again appears independent of the cell. Thus, the reconstitution of TMV particles from pure virus protein subunits and virus RNA occurs in the test tube with great ease and probably proceeds in the same automatic manner in the plant cell.

The title of this book carries the word life, which has not frequently appeared throughout its pages. The reason for this is simple. At the threshold or borderline of life, the term has little meaning and significance. To ask whether a virus is alive or dead is as pointless as to ask whether a mule is a horse or an ass, or at what stage in the metamorphosis of a tadpole we should call it a frog.

Basically, life seems to represent an intricately organized interplay of some simple chemicals with certain very complex polymers consisting largely of carbon and nitrogen compounds. Some of these polymers are able to catalyze chemical reactions and thus produce metabolism; others can contract and thus produce motion; others supply conductors. Yet accidental coalescence of a number of such active globs a few billion years ago would not have been the beginning of life, for it lacked a very important component: one that would enable the organic mass to make more of itself and thus assure its continuity beyond the time limits of stability (I almost said life expectancy) of its component molecules. Another important requirement for the development of life was that this continuity assuring agent was fallible and made mistakes. For otherwise, life would have become fixed and arrested at the primordial replicating glob stage. Thus, the functions now carried by nucleic acids, namely their ability to replicate, to carry genetic information, and to mutate, are as crucial for the process of life as are the functions of the proteins in organizing structure, metabolism, action, and reaction. Viruses, as stated, represent packaged nucleic acids, and nucleic acids are charter members of the club we call life. In their overcoats and off the club premises, the viruses are just ordinary molecular complexes. But when stripped for integrated action in close concert with enzyme proteins and other factors, viruses represent powerful and lively agents.

Because of their location on the threshold between the

living and the nonliving, viruses represent objects full of
fascination and challenge to man and his sciences. As
disease-causing agents they are far more invulnerable than
the microorganisms, because of the way in which they com-
mandeer the host's own metabolic machinery and, at times,
integrate themselves into the host's genetic apparatus. As
models for genes, each packaged with one gene-product protein, they are of incalculable value for research into the
mysteries of the mechanism of heredity. As all other agents
and causes of disease become progressively abolished, genetic defects and degenerations will loom ever more importantly as a threat to mankind. It is not yet known to
what extent cancer and many other degenerative diseases
are genetically controlled or triggered, but it is almost certain that the study of viruses and of biologically active nucleic acids will advance our understanding of these conditions. However, it seems of similar if not greater importance to this author that each small advance in this type of
research satisfies man's curiosity about his environment and
replaces an area of ignorance by one of knowledge. Gradually, there emerges an understanding of this greatest wonder of the world, the complexity of natural structure and
function climaxing in the process of life, which, with its
controlled force, delicate precision, and vast adaptability,
surpasses the whole field of modern technological wonders.

Supplementary Reading

STANLEY, W. M., and VALENS, E. G. "Viruses and the Nature of Life." E. P. Dutton, New York, 1961.

SCHUSTER, H. The RNA of viruses. *In* "The Nucleic Acids" (E. Chargaff and J. N. Davidson, eds.), Vol. III, p. 245. Academic Press, New York, 1960.

SINSHEIMER, R. L. Nucleic acids of the bacterial viruses. *In* "The Nucleic Acids" (E. Chargaff and J. N. Davidson, eds.), Vol. III, p. 187. Academic Press, New York, 1960.

TSUGITA, A., and FRAENKEL-CONRAT, H. Contributions from TMV studies of the problem of genetic information transfer and coding. *In* "Molecular Genetics" (J. H. Taylor, ed.). Academic Press, New York. To be published.

FRAENKEL-CONRAT, H. Infectious ribonucleic acid. *In* "Survey of Biological Progress" (B. Glass, ed.), Vol. IV, pp. 59–92. Academic Press, New York, 1962.

KLUG, A., and CASPAR, D. L. D. The structure of small viruses. *Advances in Virus Research* 7, 225 (1960).

SUTTON, H. ELDON, "Genes, Enzymes and Inherited Diseases." Holt, Rinehart and Winston, New York, 1961.

Index

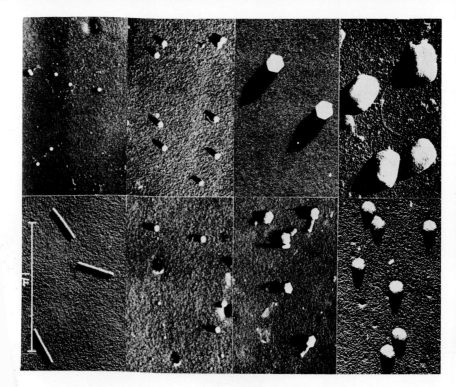

FIG. 3A

FIG. 3. *A*. *Electron micrographs of 8 typical viruses at same magnification. Top (left to right): poliomyelitis; small bacteriophage; Tipula iridescens (an insect virus, individual particles, not crystals); vaccinia. Bottom: tobacco mosaic virus; rabbit papilloma; large bacteriophage; influenza virus.*

FIG. 3. *B*. *Poliomyelitis virus; magnification: × 50,000.*

FIG. 3. *C*. *Crystalline array of poliomyelitis virus; magnification: × 115,000.*

FIG. 2. *Local lesions produced by TMV and one of its strains on a tobacco variety. A tobacco leaf (Nicotiana tabaccum var.* Xanthi) *inoculated 10 days earlier with common TMV on the left half and a chemically produced strain (nitrous acid, see p. 91) on the right half. The lesions are actually yellow-brown. Those due to common TMV are much smaller when they first appear after 3 days but continue to spread, whereas those due to some strains remain smaller, and other as tiny as those shown. The relative number of lesions is indicative of the virus concentration in the solution used for inoculating the leaf.*

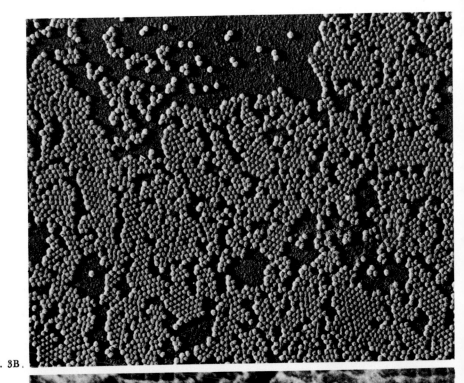

FIG. 3B

FIG. 3C

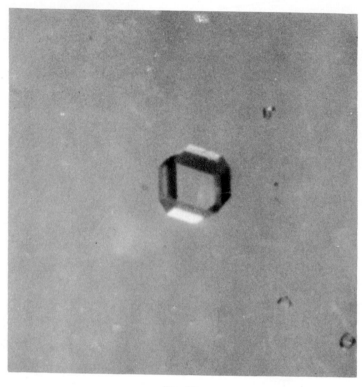

FIG. 3D

FIG. 3. D. A crystal of poliomyelitis virus as seen with the light microscope; magnification: × 250.

FIG. 3. E. Electron micrograph of TMV obtained by new technique of staining with phosphotungstate. The longest straight rod in the picture is 0.45 μ long, 50% longer than the typical length of RNA containing virus rods. The helical stacking of subunits and the central channel, here outlined by a coat of contrasting phosphotungstate solution, are clearly visible.

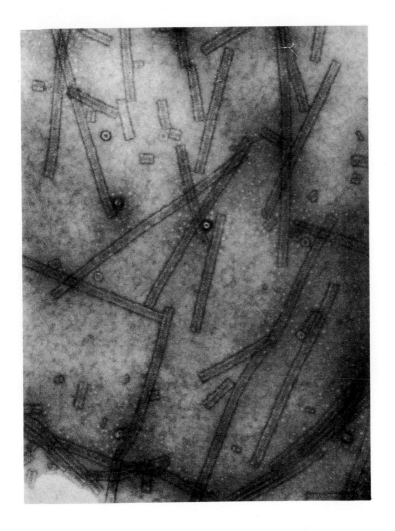

Fig. 3E

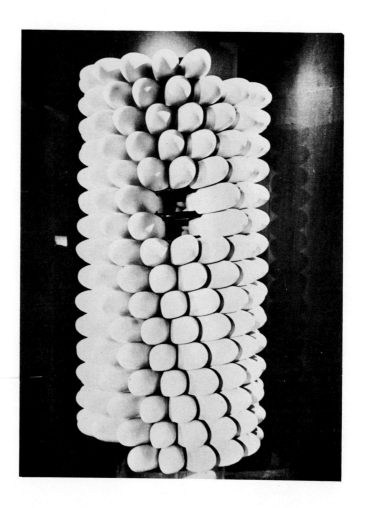

Fig. 4. Model of the structure of TMV. The white objects represent the peptide chains of the protein coat; the black tube, the RNA. Only a short segment (15 turns of the 130 turns of the helix) of the virus particle is shown. Actually, the complete rod contains 2200 peptide chains, and its proportions are those shown in Fig. 18C.

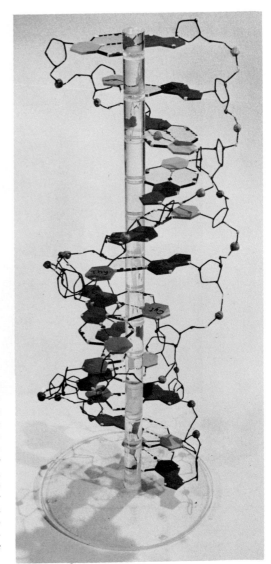

FIG. 15. *Atomic model of the double stranded helix of DNA. This model illustrates in proper relative dimensions the structure symbolized in Fig. 14. The "shelves" of interacting bases, perpendicular to the long axis of the helix, are clearly evident. It is also clear that there is "room" for attachment of other chain molecules within this framework, which is probably a biologically important feature of the structure of DNA.*

FIG. 18A

FIG. 18. *Reconstitution of a TMV particle from its components. The "co-centric" aggregation of protein subunits (peptitude chains), the white bodies, as aided and abetted by the long thread of RNA, is illustrated with models. The reaction proceeds (Fig. 18, A to J) under the influence of slightly elevated temperatures and at suitable salt concentration and neutral pH. Complete rods begin to appear within minutes.*

FIG. 18B

FIG. 18C

FIG. 18D

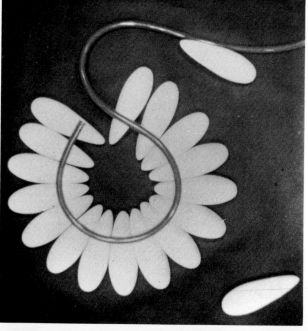

FIG. 18E

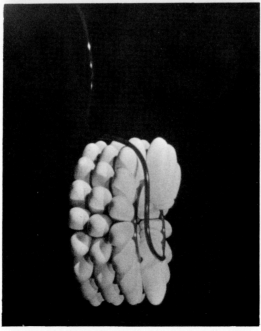

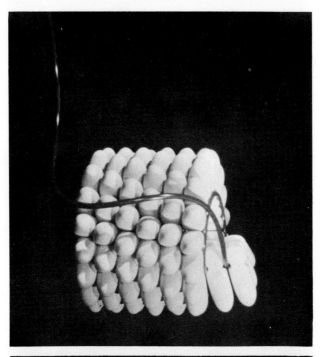

FIG. 18H

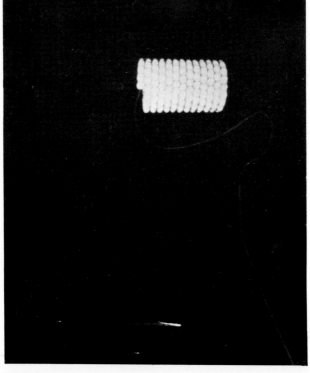

FIG. 18I

FIG. 18J

FIG. 19. *Partly degraded TMV showing threadlike RNA molecules. The virus was partly degraded by a brief treatment with a hot solution of a detergent by Dr. R. Hart. The thin threads of RNA which are visible have remained anchored in undegraded segments of the virus particles. The longest threads were measured to approach the 3000 mμ calculated for completely stretched-out chains of 6500 nucleotides. The RNA coiled up inside the virus particle, and thus also the particle, is only one-tenth as long, a little longer than the diameter of the white spheres representing polystyrene latex markers (280 mμ).*

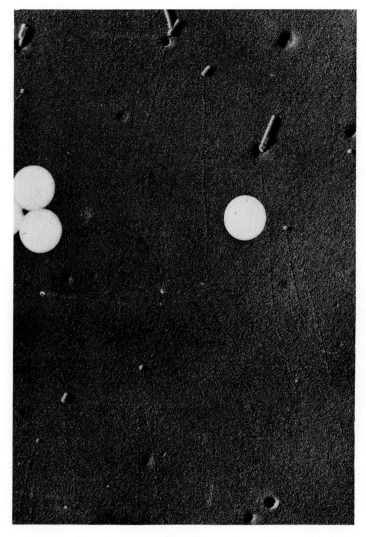

Fig. 19

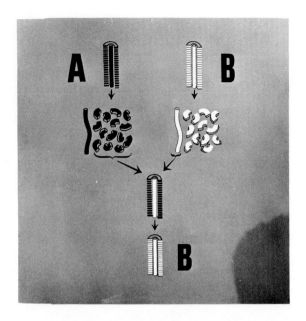

Fig. 20. *Reconstitution of mixed virus and the nature of its progeny. A and B represent two strains of TMV. Both are degraded into protein and RNA (represented as circular segments and an exhaust-pipe-like body, respectively). Reconstitution of the protein from strain A with the RNA from strain B yields a mixed virus. This, upon inoculation, yields disease symptoms characteristic of strain B, and the progeny virus isolated from such plants is indistinguishable from strain B in all respects, including the nature of the protein coat. The "mixed virus," which exists only in the test tube and loses its identity upon contact with the host, has been left nameless in the above diagram.*

Date Due

APR 1 2			
APR 3 '68			
APR 17 '68			
OCT 30 '69			
JUN 1 8 '74			
OCT 1 6 '74			

WITHDRAWN
THE COLLEGE AT BROCKPORT
DRAKE MEMORIAL LIBRARY

Library Bureau Cat. No. 1137